THE
LOTTERIE$

THE
LOTTERIE$

by Daoma Winston

WILLIAM MORROW AND COMPANY, INC.
New York

PROLOGUE

CHAPTER 364 was presented to both houses of the Assembly on May 3, 1974. It allowed the operation of lotteries by and for the benefit of the State, and established a Commission to devise and run such lotteries, the profits of which would go to the General Fund.

EXCERPTS from the debate on CHAPTER 364.

PRO:

MR. SPEAKER: Our property owners are over-taxed. We need new revenue. A lottery will provide it, allowing those with hope in their hearts to put out their small hostages to fortune, for the benefit of the State. I say 'Yes' to CHAPTER 364.

CON:

MR. SPEAKER: A lottery is an unproductive and immoral game, opening the door to corruption and crime. It is a regressive tax, taking from those whose despair leads to hopeless dreams. I say 'No' to CHAPTER 364.

On May 5, 1974, both houses of the Assembly passed CHAPTER 364 establishing a State Lottery.

Sale of tickets began on New Year's Day, January 1, 1976, and has continued to date.

THE
LOTTERIE$

CHAPTER 1

Later Quinn Monroe would remember that the nightmare began with no real warning. It was February, early in that short month of short days.

There was an inconsequential conversation, and in the background the four-fifteen Saturday-afternoon news report which concerned the usual mixture of impersonal and distant disaster: Terrorist killings. SALT talks in Moscow. Panama Canal arguments in Washington. And, closer to home, Indian land claims in the state capital at St. Mary's City.

She heard the facts, but didn't think about them. She no longer cared about Moscow, Panama, or even Washington. St. Mary's City was a place she went to twice a month, on her own business.

Helen Martenson also ignored the news. She sipped black coffee, then said, "So, when I was divorced, I came back to Elkhorn." Her paint-smeared hand made a circular gesture that stood for the hundred-year-old barn now converted to a house. "This was all I had."

Quinn said nothing. The radio newscast covered her silence by announcing that the previous year's profit of two million dollars had been returned to the state general fund by the Lottery Commission. The New England weather forecast was for more snow after midnight, and rising tides along the coast.

"But I've found it lonely," Helen went on. "I'm sure you do, too."

The tone conveyed the motherly interest suitable to a woman of Helen's age. She was forty-eight, her hair frosted. But her face had the look of a teenager avid for an hour's confidences.

Quinn smoothed the paper-thin veal slices she had just cut. She found a tenderizer mallet in a drawer beneath the sink. She said finally, "I've been too busy getting to know my way around, and with the job, to think of that."

"That's another thing. So much driving . . . Passamody, Riverton, St. Mary's City . . . If you'd stay put in Elkhorn, you could have some social life. Which is what you need."

Between thumps of the mallet, Quinn answered, "I like the traveling."

"But you've been here four months and haven't made a single friend," Helen protested.

By friend, Helen meant men. She waited. Quinn didn't answer. That was something she wasn't going to talk about.

Finally Helen said, "Tell me, Quinn. What really happened to Jenny Lakas anyway?"

Quinn's hand froze on the mallet. It came down with a thump that tore the meat. Held fast in a chill tremor, she couldn't speak. Jenny Lakas was another something she wasn't going to talk about.

Helen sighed, "Never mind. I didn't mean to pry. But you're so self-contained. Not like me."

It was true. Within hours after Quinn's arrival, she knew all about Helen, whose confidences had made Quinn uneasy then, just as her probing made Quinn uneasy now.

But she forced a smile, set the mallet in the sink. "I guess I don't have much to tell."

"Of course you do. You're just not ready yet."

Another reference to Jenny. This time indirect. Irene must have written of her to Helen. It couldn't be helped.

In the face of Quinn's silence, Helen sighed again. "Oh, well, back to the salt mines."

Alone. The kitchen silent except for the beat of music. Quinn turned the radio off. She salted and peppered the meat and put it away. When she reached for the bottle of Marsala, she found it empty.

She went into the central living area, where Helen's angry paintings hung on the walls.

Helen was warming her hands at the Franklin stove. She saw the bottle Quinn still held. "Oh-oh, I'm sorry. I forgot I'd finished it. Give me a minute to clean up and I'll run down to Cory's to get some."

"It's okay," Quinn said. "I'll go." While Helen murmured weak protests, Quinn pulled on heavy boots, stuffed herself into a thick ski sweater, and zipped a fleece-lined parka over it. As she stepped into the icy wind, she pushed her loose red-gold hair under the roll of a knit stocking cap.

Later she would remember that that was how the nightmare began. With an inconsequential conversation, a radio newscast, and an empty bottle of wine.

* * *

Some seventy miles north of Elkhorn the All-State Turnpike circled the town of Riverton. But the Turnpike Diner had been built on its periphery. At off times, such as now on a Saturday afternoon, the rumble of the big trucks became a soothing background to the clatter of flatware taken through the three-rinse routine by a tired Indian girl in the kitchen.

Through the serving window in the wall behind the counter, Mary Baker caught a glimpse of the girl's languid movements. Mary remembered when she, too, had washed dishes in a diner much like this one. She didn't realize that with the recollection her Cupid's-bow mouth drooped, her blue eyes darkened.

But Shirley Bacon, the waitress, saw the change in Mary's face. She said, "She's going to make the same mistake you did."

Mary looked at the diner's only other customer. He sat at the end of the counter, his head in a paperback book. Then, to Shirley: "Anything's better than being back there with the steam and the stink. And who says I made a mistake?"

"People never learn," Shirley retorted. "Sixteen! What does she know? What did you know when you picked Gus?"

"I knew what I wanted and needed. And it sure wasn't any mistake. Gus is good to me."

"But what you could have been," Shirley murmured.

Mary dimpled. "You just want to make me feel good."

"Feel good? I'm trying to make you feel bad. I'm trying to get through your pretty but thick skull that—"

"Shirley, please." Mary put down her empty cup, glanced at the wall clock. "I guess I'd better go. He'll be home soon."

Shirley wasn't to be stopped. "What you could have been—that's what I keep thinking. Look at yourself sometime. Your hair's gorgeous—that blue-black color. And not out of a bottle either. And your navy-blue eyes. Not to mention the shape."

"You're teasing. And I don't like it." But the dimples remained in Mary's cheeks. She couldn't help it, even if she felt disloyal to Gus when she listened. Shirley just made her feel good.

"It's the truth. With your looks, you could have gone anywhere, done anything. So you married at sixteen and ended up in Riverton, and here you are, at twenty-four, your whole life ahead of you. And you're still stuck in Riverton."

"I want to be. I've got what I need." Except for one single thing, Mary thought. But she didn't know how to get that any more than she knew how to do much of anything else. How could she? When Gus did everything?

"Modeling," Shirley said dreamily. "You could do that for sure. You're a perfect six, almost."

"Almost is right. I'm too broad in the bottom for a six these days."

"You don't have to be if you don't want to be." Shirley went to refill the coffee cup of the man at the other end of the counter. Returning, she went on, "And maybe TV. You'd be great in the perfume commercials. Let your hair grow long, see. Take off your bra—"

"Oh, Shirley." Part giggle, part protest.

"Of course you'd have to get in shape. A little diet and exercise for the bottom. And lotion on your hands. You can't have working hands. And to grow your hair. But it doesn't add up to much."

"Just too much." Mary glanced at the clock again. "Maybe I better go. When he works overtime he usually quits at four."

"And what about the three-beer stop on the way home?"

"Oh, well." Mary relaxed on the stool. "Half an hour more or less doesn't matter anyhow."

Shirley's shrug said it all. *She* wouldn't have a husband who stopped for a few beers after work. *She* wouldn't have a man who wanted his hamburger hot and ready and on the table within minutes after he'd scrubbed his hands. *She* wouldn't be married to Gus Baker.

Mary looked into the dregs of her coffee. It was a pity that they didn't like each other. Shirley and Gus. The three of them could have been such good friends.

The diner's door groaned open, sighed shut. A guard from the shoe factory across the road came in, blowing white plumes of visible breath.

Shirley grinned at him, swooped to set up three coffees to go, wrapped sweet rolls in paper. She moved like a dancer, quick, graceful, her big breasts bobbing over the tightly belted waist of her uniform, her hips flaring out, rounded. Her hair was raven black, elaborately curled in forehead bangs, and fell in a heavy shoulder-length pageboy. It was a style she had copied from the picture of a late-forties movie star, but it suited her sultry face. Her eyes were black, too, knowing. Her mouth was mobile, with strong expressive lips. She had been married three times, had been to California and back. She was free now to do as she pleased, and did, and boasted about it whenever she got the chance. She never said that discontent ate in her like a tapeworm. She hardly knew it. But it made her a troublemaker, a spoiler, a ruffler of calm waters. She called it speaking her mind, and being herself, and getting what she wanted out of life.

When the guard left, Mary shivered in the cold draft, took a quick gulp of coffee. Then she got to her feet, buttoning her coat. It wasn't a long walk to the trailer park, but twilight had given way to early dark. It would be hard to keep to the road shoulder with only sparse traffic to show the way. She wished now that she had gone earlier. But it was always the same. She hated leaving.

Shirley returned to ask, "Going now?"

"Have to."

"I'm off days next week. Want to do something special?"

"Sure." And, without thinking, "Make it my treat this time, though. Let's go to the Greentree Club for lunch."

"The Greentree?" Shirley grinned. "Can you really spring for that?"

"I suggested it."

"Thank you! It's the best offer I've had in weeks," Shirley said, adding as Mary turned toward the door, "And I won't tell Gus, either."

Mary pretended she hadn't heard. She let the door shut behind her. From the turnpike there came the trumpeting horn of a semi. The faint stink of diesel oil hung on the air. The road was empty, dark. She set out, walking as quickly as she could.

Soon lights flickered behind her, drew closer and rose, bathing her in a white glare, and throwing her shadow long and slim and fast-moving before her.

She was frightened before she had reason to be. Then the lights stayed on her. Tires crunched slowly alongside.

Now she knew she had reason. Sweat poured down between her shoulder blades. Her throat dried. She prayed for another car to come by.

"Hey, honey, want a ride?"

She was deaf, stone-deaf.

"It's a cold night, baby. Where you want to go?"

She stared before her, blind.

"Just say and we'll take you."

She was mute. She couldn't even scream.

The car rolled slowly, kept up with her brisk straining steps. The door opened. An arm came out, reaching. "Come on, honey. Let's have some fun."

A chorus of laughter. Two men. Maybe three. Showing off for each other.

Sudden lights ahead. She was free. She spun away from the reaching hand, leaped for the center of the road. No longer mute, she screamed. No longer deaf, she heard the yell, "Goddamn bitch!"

The car sped away.

The lights that had saved her were on a truck. It slowed. Its horn beeped. She shivered as it swung around her and disappeared into the dark. She moved to the shoulder, looked ahead. Nothing.

Fighting back tears, she went on. She was rigid with fear until she saw the glow of the trailer park. As she turned into it, the dogs began to yowl.

The door was unlocked. She stepped inside, closed it gently behind her. Home. Safe. And Gus was here before her.

She took off her pink scarf, and used it to wipe the sweat from her cheeks. She heard the shower, his voice, bass and off-key bellowing a song. Still shivering, her hands atremble, she got out of her coat, and put it into the narrow closet.

He'd be scrubbing off the grease with Go-Jo. He'd be patting forward some of his longer back hair to hide the thinning place in front. He'd slather on cologne, and come out hungry after the day's work.

She made hamburgers, dropped frozen fries into a pan, turned the fire on under the coffee pot. She wouldn't think of what had happened on the road. She wouldn't tell him. He'd say it was Shirley's fault for keeping her too late at the diner. He'd say he didn't want her to be Shirley's friend anymore.

Gus came out in Jockey shorts, his bare chest covered with a thick mat of coppery hair. He grinned. "Hi, kind of late, aren't you?"

"Dinner's almost ready."

"I wasn't talking about dinner."

She didn't answer. She folded green napkins and set them beside green plates.

He seemed to fill the galley. He watched her. "What's wrong?"

"Nothing, Gus."

"How come I don't get a kiss?"

She forced a grin. "How come you didn't ask for it?"

"I didn't know I had to." One step brought him to her. His big calloused hands slid from her shoulders to her buttocks, drawing her close to him. "Hey, it's Saturday. It's been a long hard week."

Even while he held her, she felt the fear she had known on the road. A stranger's body pressed to hers. She whispered, "The fries, Gus."

"I like them well done."

"The hamburgers," she said faintly.

"I'll take them well done, too." But he reached past her to turn off the gas jets. He drew her into the living room, to the built-in sofa that was wide enough for a single body. He felt her small resistance. "Damn it, what's the matter with you, Mary?"

"I thought you'd want your dinner."

"To hell with my goddam dinner." He pushed her down to the sofa, stared at her, green eyes alight behind stubby coppery lashes. "Jesus," he said. "Jesus, what am I going to do with you? It's Shirley, isn't it? Every time you see her, you're like this."

"It's not," Mary cried.

"Arguing. All the time now, this arguing with me. Shirley."

"Stop it! You don't know what happened," Mary said, knowing she'd have to tell him because Shirley wasn't to blame. Sobbing, Mary managed to get it out.

He listened, gradually moving closer until he picked her up, and sat holding her on his lap. But when her voice faded into a shivering silence, he said, "I told you not to walk these roads after dark. I've said it a hundred times. Now will you listen to me? If anything had happened it would have been Shirley's fault."

From Riverton, the All-State went arrow-straight to St. Mary's City, taking a short bypass around its most affluent suburb. It was called Belair, and lay on a ridge that overlooked the town, with a view that included the lit dome of the state capitol. On this late Saturday afternoon, it seemed to float in a white mist.

Adelaide Herman absently noticed it when she closed the drapes against the early dark. Her full attention was on the diamond ring she wore. It was a beautiful thing.

She knew that her husband was watching her, but she didn't speak as she turned from the window.

"You like that ring," George said. "Enjoy it while you can."

"George," she sighed. "What do you want?"

He could have told her, "Love me. That's all I ever wanted." Instead he answered, "I don't know. I don't even know why I talk like that."

She shook her biond head. Her blue eyes were narrowed in contempt. "You want sympathy. You want me to figure out what to do."

He gave a short ugly laugh. "I wish you could."

"So do I. But I have no suggestions. And I'm not going to make a fool of myself by offering you my shoulder to cry on."

"I didn't ask for that."

"You'd take it if you could."

"Damn you, Adelaide."

"You've been saying that for years, George."

"Don't tell anybody. It'll be a catastrophe if the word gets around."

"I won't say a word, George."

"You'd better not, if you want to have anything left." He sank into a deep velvet easy chair, sighed. "If only there was somewhere to turn. A little more time."

"Yes," she agreed absently.

"And something to start with. But God, everything's tied up. And the bills . . ."

She glared at him. "Are you saying it's my fault?"

"No. It's *my* fault," he retorted. "*I'm* the one who had to give Evan that station wagon he totaled in a week. *I'm* the one that had to send him to a fancy private school. *I'm* the one who had to have the diamond ring you're wearing."

"*You* gave him the car to replace the station wagon. *You* wanted him to go to that school. *You* gave me the ring."

"Only to shut you up!"

"Why don't you figure out what to do instead of blaming me?" she demanded.

"If I could I would, damn you!"

Her slender silk-clad shoulders went rigid. She gave him a glance of distaste. "It always comes down to cursing. You can't discuss anything without it."

"You used to like my swearing."

"I've learned to hate it during twenty-two years of marriage."

"I thought you'd settled for having Evan be the gentleman in the family."

"Stop bringing him into this. He has nothing to do with it." And, sighing, "I don't know what's the matter with you."

"I'm worried," George answered.

"So you've told me for weeks." Her eyes went to the thick draperies at the windows, then to the dense plush rug at her feet. She looked at the guns over the mantel. She had hated them since George put them up on racks after a burglary years before. He'd refused to take them down. They represented his success to him. They meant he had something to protect. Still looking at them, she said, "We could have a garage sale, I suppose. And start off with your guns."

"I've just told you nobody's to know."

"Then that won't do, will it?" She shrugged. "If you won't let me help, then I guess I'll just have to sit and wait for you to ruin us."

His big jowly face reddened. "If I had half of what you've gone through in the last twenty-two years—"

"George Herman, you knew what I was when we married!"

"And you knew what I was. You haven't let me forget it for one goddamn minute!"

It was on the tip of her tongue to say it all. To tell him what she'd known for years, and how she felt about it. Only the same old anguish, the same pride, kept her silent. But she had to get away from him. She went to the door.

He demanded, "Where are you going?"

"Into the dining room. Evan's coming for dinner."

George frowned. "I wonder what he wants this time."

"*I* didn't spoil him."

"That means *I* did, I guess," George yelled.

"For once we agree." Before he could answer, Adelaide stepped into the hall and closed the door softly between them.

George got up heavily, a big man, thick in the shoulders and waist, moving with the soft tread of a bear. He went to the window, pulled back the velvet drape, and stared at the lit dome of the capitol, asking himself how it could have happened.

The location was perfect. Just east of the city. Electric power lines close by. Sewer hookups easily arranged for. The land priced right for one-acre-lot houses. The house design exactly what the state capital needed. It was booming, while the rest of the state stood still. Lumber mills closing. Pulp mills mostly gone. Shoe factories producing a quarter of what they once had. Unemployment rates shooting up. But the capital was based on an industry that continued to grow. The bureaucrats and the lobbyists increased, and both could afford good well-built homes. If the houses had all sold, he'd be on Easy

Street, and he and Adelaide would be as polite to each other as they had been before. But only five out of twenty-five had gone. He wasn't covered.

Labor costs had risen. Material, too. Lumber. Concrete. Insulation. Glass. Paint. A penny here, a dime there. His original estimates were worthless now. His credit gone. His dream, what he'd named Hermad Estates, was about to go down the drain.

He was thinking of that when he heard Evan's car in the drive.

The sky was dim over the inland city called Windsor. Nathaniel Gordon looked out the window at waning twilight. "I won't," he said. "It's not even five o'clock. Why should I go to bed?"

Firm fingers tightened around his wrist in an angry pressure taking his angry pulse. But the aide's voice was sweetened with artificial sugar, saying, "It's over a hundred, Mr. Gordon. This has been a difficult day for you."

"My pulse is always quick," he retorted.

The aide was named Margery Bestow. He called her "Bastard" in his mind. She had a narrow mouth, and no bosom. Her fingernails were too long for her work. While she counted his pulse with false solicitude, he wondered how soon he'd call her Bastard aloud.

Johanna Smithy, another aide, paused in the doorway. "Trouble?"

"Old men find change difficult," Margery said.

Nathaniel closed his eyes. They spoke as if he were deaf, dumb, and blind. As if he had no heart, and no feelings. Bastard, he thought. Smutty, he thought.

"Old women are harder to handle," Johanna was saying. "But when you come to think of it, there's not much difference between the two, is there?" She giggled. "The vital something's gone."

"That's what you think," Nathaniel said balefully, opening his eyes.

Johanna turned toward Margery. "The men'll be coming any minute. Better get him into bed and out of the way."

"Ridiculous," Nathaniel growled. "Why shove me in at five o'clock on a Saturday afternoon?"

"One hundred and twenty-seven this time," Margery told him triumphantly. "You must be a good boy this evening."

"The Jets are playing at five. It's going to be on television. I never miss their games."

"You will this time. There won't be television at five o'clock."

"Who says? Why not?" he demanded.

"Mrs. Leggette, the administrator, that's who says. And because. That's why not." Margery dropped his wrist, tugged at his arm. "Now we must settle you quickly. We wouldn't want to have an accident, would we?"

"Get me out of the way of what?"

"The furniture movers, Mr. Gordon." Margery drew him toward the bed. Her fingers went to his tie.

He brushed her hand away. "Young lady, if I may call you that, I am able to disrobe on my own. And able, too, to decide when I want to. I don't want to now. And I won't."

"I did expect your cooperation, Mr. Gordon."

"I'll sit quietly out of the way," he told her. He was furious now. His face was flushed. His pale eyes glittered. What were they up to?

"I suppose that'd be all right. But don't fail me. There are ways to deal with recalcitrant patients."

"I'm not a patient. I'm a resident." Then: "What do you mean?"

"In such institutions as this there are always a few irresponsibles. Not that they can help it. We all understand, being trained to recognize those patients unable to take orders and cooperate, or to think clearly for themselves."

"Are you threatening me?" he asked softly.

"I'm saying that things are different now at Roseview. We'll do everything to keep the patients happy. But National Nursing Homes Company, Inc., NNHC for short, has its own policy, which is based on the latest studies in geriatrics."

"Geriatrics?"

"Medicine for the old."

There was the tramp of feet in the corridor. A loud clatter as something metal slammed into a wall.

Within half an hour, as Nathaniel watched in disbelief, his pleasant two-man room was converted into an overcrowded cell. It surprised him that no bars had yet appeared at the windows.

The easy chair that had been his wife Minerva's was gone. The rosewood desk at which he had done his monthly accounts for as long as he could remember was gone. Now there were four iron beds, four impossibly tiny tables. And no space left in which a man could stretch.

Margery appeared on the threshold. "You should rest until the supper bell at six, Mr. Gordon."

He said nothing, but as her rubber-soled shoes whispered away he declared war. He waited until he was certain she had gone downstairs before he took up the cane he had used for the past ten years to help strengthen his weakened left leg. He went slowly down the steps and into the empty recreation room.

It was dark. But he needed no light. He picked his path between chairs and tables. He turned on the set, waited expectantly for the warm-up hum. Nothing happened. Frowning, he went to the wall socket. The plug had been pulled, the wire draped over the console. He imagined the Bastard's satisfied smile. She had enjoyed doing this. Carefully he first adjusted the volume to low, then set the plug into its socket. When the screen brightened, he sank into a close-by chair.

Later the door opened. The light flashed on. He didn't turn his head. The Jets were having a free-for-all on the screen. Hockey sticks and curses were flying.

"Mr. Gordon!"

He rose slowly, leaning on his cane, to confront a pale Johanna Smithy. He stared at her forbiddingly.

"We'll see about this!" she cried.

"It's Saturday's best show."

"You know the new rules."

"Damn your new rules. This is my *home,* woman."

Her mouth turned down. "We don't allow bad language, Mr. Gordon." She trotted away.

He limped slowly to the door. War was tiring, he'd suddenly learned. He was at the steps when Mrs. Leggette caught up with him. A tall, very stout woman with tiny eyes and a few straggly hairs on her upper lip. He hated tall, stout, hairy women.

"A word with you," she said.

"You may have several. So long as I have a few in return."

"I don't make bargains." Her glance met his, slipped away. "Johanna. A chair. Mr. Gordon is tired."

The wheelchair hissed behind him. He took a step. "I'm not that tired." But he toppled backward to the sudden pressure behind his knees. His cane dropped away with a clatter.

Before he knew what had happened, both his hands were bound to the chair arms with wide gauze straps.

Lenore Leggette met his eyes, and this time she didn't look away. She said softly, but overclearly, as if speaking to a child, "You're plainly unable to understand our rules. So you must be restrained for your own safety. It's only until you learn to adjust. Then we'll be happy to see you on your feet again."

He pursed his lips. Lenore Leggette. Louse.

Johanna pushed him into the small elevator on which, as a matter of pride, he had never before ridden. It was for invalids and chairs. He wasn't one and had never needed one.

The skirmish was over, he conceded silently, but the battle had just begun.

It was the same Saturday evening, but fifteen hundred miles away in the country's heartland, a small Kansas town. A wind white with snow flung itself down the obsolete highway that was Kenyon's main street. It lathered frost on unlit neon signs over abandoned garages, and laid fringes of lace on the thick she-oaks that had seen the once bustling railhead dwindle to nothing over two generations. It hissed through the bare rose trellis that clung to the Lakas house.

Inside, Mortimer Lakas stared at the television screen. He didn't have to look at his wife Elvira to know what she was doing. As soon as he heard the first faint whisper of her movements, he understood. His mouth tightened. His pale gray eyes narrowed behind steel-rimmed spectacles. The chink of the vase. The rustle of the lace scarf on the table top. Now the hinge would squeal on the china closet. Scrape, slide, drawer squeaks. The noises came in rapid succession as she made quick darts here and there.

"Elvira," he said irritably. "Come on, settle down and watch with me."

"But it's so funny," she protested. "I know they were here. Every one of them in those little silver frames I used to buy in Kansas City. They were all here, Mort. I just don't know where they've gone."

"You don't even remember when you last saw them," he told her. "Neither do I."

"Yes. I know," she answered. "But they *were* here."

Listening from the shadows in the hall, Jerry Lakas smiled. She could look forever. She'd never find them. He practiced an innocent face. And if she asked him . . . But she wouldn't of course. Not Elvira. Neither would Mort. His parents were like that. They would pretend, to him at least, that nothing was missing. That nothing was wrong. That's what they'd always done.

Jerry went soundlessly to the door, eased it open, and stepped out into the cold. He didn't feel the snow on his cheeks or the pummeling of the wind.

In the parlor behind him, Elvira stopped, leaned one hand on the dusty piano. "Was that Jerry?"

Mortimer didn't answer.

"Where do you suppose he's going now?"

"I don't know. I never can figure him out, and you can't either."

Mortimer and Elvira had been a little afraid of him for years. It was not from what he had said or done, but something in his look that they didn't understand. It had begun a long time before, when he and Jenny were young. They didn't know why exactly, but they blamed him for what had happened to Jenny, and that had scared them, too. They never spoke of it, but they both breathed easier when Jerry was out.

With his eyes blinking against the snow, he made his way to the garage behind the house. He climbed into the back seat of the sedan and put his small transistor radio beside him, absently tuning it in. When the music drowned the whine of the wind, he leaned to lift up one corner of the front seat. Slowly, one after another, he took out some of the treasure he had hidden there.

Pale light gleamed on tarnished silver. Small Jenny, nine months old, clutching his nose and grinning, while he held her on his lap. He still felt the heat of her in his groin. They had brought her home from the hospital, and put her tiny body into his arms, and said, "Look, this is your baby sister. She's all yours, Jerry." Jenny, dancing in a flame-red gypsy costume at Halloween . . . standing on her hands in the back yard . . . proud and straight in her white high school graduation robe . . .

He studied each one, his eyes filling until slow silent tears rose up and overflowed, leaving silver trails on his unshaven cheeks.

Finally he squeezed his eyes shut. But he could still see. Now there were blinking blue lights and a tall slender girl with reddish-gold hair walking between two policemen. She had shared a life with Jenny. A life he didn't know. Her name whispered itself as a cold wind through his mind. Quinn Monroe.

In the parlor, Elvira said tiredly, "I'm sure I'll find them sometime, someplace."

Mortimer didn't answer.

"It seems so long," she went on. "But I can't stop hoping."

"Six months," Mortimer told her. "And you know as well as I do that we've got nothing to hope for any more."

The scrape of the vase. The rustle of the scarf. She said, "I'll find them."

"The pictures," Mortimer told her. "Maybe, that is."

It wasn't necessary to say the rest of it. Unspoken, the truth lay between them, heaving in the still air. She might find the silver-framed photographs. But that was all she'd find of what she sought.

It was too late to hope for Jenny, to look for her. Jenny wasn't coming home again.

CHAPTER 2

Quinn switched the car heater to high. Even after four months, she continued to feel a New England chill deep in her bones.

The Rabbit, a highly visible apple green, purred as she drove through the gap in the stone fence and into the curved lane. On both sides of it were snowy fields that glistened blue in the early twilight.

She drew a deep contented breath, enjoying the stillness. The only sound she heard was the rasp of her studded tires in the frozen ruts over which she jolted. The once familiar cry of sirens, of wailing ambulances and hooting police cruisers that had haunted her days and dreams, was no part of this soothing landscape.

Ahead of her a red taillight winked on and off on the Old North Road. She coasted to a stop at the yield sign, waited until a logging truck rumbled by, its chains clanking, its wheels flinging back a curtain of dirty sleet. When the way was clear, she maneuvered the Rabbit over the snowbank thrown up by the plowing the day before. The thick blanket of low-hanging clouds suggested that the weather report was right. The highway would be deep with a fresh fall by morning. But now it was firm, and gave her the easiest driving she had had that week, even though the light was fading fast.

She reached toward the knob on the dashboard. In the same instant, something lunged at her from the side of the road.

She froze, one hand stretched toward the lights knob, the other clutching the wheel. The car swerved hard to the left, then slid to the right, where it went suddenly aloft, flying as if weightless through unresisting air until, with another swerve, it dropped to earth, slipping hard to the right again.

Her gloved fingers felt the wheel spin. Sudden dark flowed past the windshield as the tires rasped in a snowbank. The car bottomed with an angry screech of metal burning into ice, straddled the bank, and slammed to a tilted halt.

Quinn lay across the wheel. Her knit cap had fallen off. Her long red-gold hair had tumbled down, veiling the dark bruise on her forehead.

Time stopped briefly, then swung in an impossible reverse . . .

* * *

Through unearthly silence she heard the tap of her sandals on the marble floor of the foyer. The Wallowby's heavy glass doors sighed shut behind her, sealing out the oppressive heat of a Washington summer day. A huddle of tenants she knew only by face stood near the desk, heads tipped close in whispered conversation.

She fished for her keys as she went toward the elevator corridor. Through the glass wall that showed the patio beyond, she saw the rhythmic pulse of blue dome lights. Montgomery County police. Another robbery. It was a commonplace in these close-in suburbs.

She didn't notice the resident manager until the woman plunged at her, calling, "Miss Monroe! Oh, Quinn, dear." Face gray beneath rouged cheeks. Gasping, "I tried to call you at the office. You'd left. I told the police you were on the way. It's bad news, Quinn." Tugging at Quinn's arm, the woman thrust her into the cold cushions of an easy chair.

Bad news. Quinn was suddenly limp. The two words were echoes, resonating from an autumn day seven years before when both her parents died.

"Quinn," the woman rushed on. "It's Jenny. She's dead. The police want you."

"Jenny?" Quinn demanded. "Jenny Lakas?"

"They want you out there," the resident manager answered. Now she pulled Quinn up from the chair into which she had just pushed her. "Out below the balcony."

Quinn had no time to react. A uniformed officer came toward her, bootheels firm on the floor. He had blue eyes in a pink-cheeked boyish face.

"*I* couldn't do it," the woman was saying. "You're her apartment mate. So you have to."

The officer took Quinn's elbow. He eased her with him through the glass doors. "We need a positive identification, miss."

Heavy air. A blue flickering light. Red flashes from the rescue squad ambulance. Garish camera explosions.

And then, a crumpled mass on the terrazzo.

A hand under both of Quinn's elbows as a wide-shouldered man in a sweaty shirt leaned to turn back the edge of a green blanket that covered grotesque lumps and angles. Short chestnut hair, streaked darker with blood. Red streams and smears at mouth and nose. Eyes cloudy and colorless.

"It's Jenny Lakas," Quinn whispered. Her legs melted from beneath her. She went to her knees, reaching blindly for a limp, chill hand. "Oh, Jenny, Jenny, what happened? Why did you do it?" she sobbed. "Why, Jenny? Why?"

The rescue ambulance drove away, trailing a soft mournful whine. A green sedan parked beside the cruiser that still blinked blue against the fading afternoon. Two men conferred with the uniformed policemen. Then they came to Quinn, who leaned wearily on a white fender.

"Miss Monroe? I'm Johnson. My partner's name is Jason. We're with the Montgomery County Detective Division."

Detectives. Why? Her face looked the question.

"Sudden death," Johnson said briefly. He was a black man, tall, with a deep soft voice.

Jason was chubby, blond. He nodded, didn't speak.

"You've identified the victim as Jenny Lakas, your apartment mate. That right?"

"Yes." The reply was a dry whisper.

"I don't like to bother you now, but we have to go up to your place," Johnson told her. And: "Is there someone you'd like to have with you?"

Quinn thought of her co-worker Irene Harrich, remembered she had mentioned a dinner date. The show at Blues Alley. Quinn shook her head. She moved cautiously from the fender, feeling as if the terrazzo had softened to tar that threatened to give way beneath her.

Johnson fell into step on her left, Jason on her right. The three of them went through the patio doors and into the lobby.

The twittering tenants stared.

Quinn heard the whisper of her name among them.

"All through?" the resident manager gasped.

Johnson nodded, but when she asked, "Shall I come up?" he looked into Quinn's face and saw her mute refusal. He said, "No, thanks. We'll manage."

For the second time Quinn searched out her keys. She clasped them in cold fingers while the elevator glided to the fourteenth floor.

She opened the apartment door, fumbling at the two locks. A hot wet wind blasted through the living room from the balcony. She looked that way, then sank into the sofa, eyes closed.

"You mind if we go ahead?" Johnson asked.

She shrugged. She was bruised, aching. She thought of the first time she had seen Jenny. A gusty March night. Jenny was breathless,

her chestnut hair wind-tousled. She came in, apologizing for bein[g]
late.

"It doesn't matter," Quinn told her. "I'm home for the evenin[g]
Did you have trouble finding the apartment?"

"No. But I asked a few times just to make sure."

"Would you like to look around?" Quinn had offered. "Or mayb[e]
have a cup of coffee first?"

Smiling, Jenny had stripped off her bright-red coat. "Coffee wou[ld]
be nice." And, seated at the breakfast bar, "Have you been he[re]
long?"

"About five years."

"I like your things," Jenny said, her gray eyes on the china cup[s.]

"They belonged to my parents," Quinn answered. And: "They[re]
dead." It had taken years to learn to say that. She still couldn't e[x-]
plain.

"I've never managed to accumulate anything but clothes. T[oo]
much moving around, I guess."

"I've always wanted to travel." A flicker of memory . . . [a]
globe spinning under her father's hand . . . Jaipur, and hooded [co-]
bras rising from baskets to a reedy tune . . . She went on: "Wha[t I]
want to do is go around the world. And someday I will." A prom[ise]
she had made to him. To herself, too.

Jenny laughed. "As soon as your treasure-laden ship comes i[n."]

When they had finished the coffee, Quinn led the way to the b[ed]
room. Twin beds in two corners, two dressers that didn't mat[ch.]
Gold curtains and spreads.

"Everything's included," she said, adding, out of a single bitter [ex-]
perience, "except long-distance calls."

Jenny grinned. "I don't make them." She nodded briskly. "I lik[e it]
here." She cocked a brow at Quinn. "And I like you, too. The o[nly]
thing is, will my hours bother you? My shifts at the hospital chan[ge.]
You can never depend on me to be in." She paused. "Or out, for t[hat]
matter."

"No problem," Quinn answered.

They discussed the rent, the availability of laundry facilities do[wn]
the hall, the bus schedules.

Jenny wrote a check, handed it to Quinn. "Until tomorrow, th[en.]
I'll arrive with bag and baggage at close to six."

Five months later, on a hot smoggy August day, Jenny died.

Quinn crouched in the sofa, suddenly aware of muffled footsteps, murmurings.

Then: "Purse here on the chair." And: "Yes. Social Security card." Soon after: "No cigarettes in the ashtray. No drink glasses." More footsteps, Johnson said clearly, "See this? Where she stood. And here's where she climbed over. That's her skirt sliding across the soot. Here's where she held on, facing inside. Yeah. Palm prints."

"Um," Jason agreed, the first sound he'd made.

Quinn hadn't known it was going to happen so she wasn't prepared to fight it. She coughed and couldn't breathe. Sobs wracked her.

A brown hand thrust tissue at her. She buried her face in it. Within moments, a soft "Um," signaled Jason's presence at her side. He gave her coffee. She accepted it. She concentrated on getting it down. Even then, though, she was aware of further rustlings, quiet footsteps.

"Better?" Johnson asked finally.

She nodded, looked for Jason, but didn't see him.

"We've been over the apartment," Johnson told her. "There's no note."

Quinn stared at him.

At last he said, "We're sure nobody was here with her, but since there's nothing . . ." He let the words hang. Then: "Maybe you could tell us why she'd do it."

Quinn's mind was blank. Jenny . . . coming, going. Brief conversations about the weather, traffic, a difficult patient. A red flared skirt that needed lengthening.

"No," Quinn said. "I can't imagine. She never seemed depressed, or—or anything but what she always was."

"And what was that?"

"Nice. Very friendly. But always on the run."

"How long has she lived with you?"

"Since March. We'd been sharing the rent."

"Five months." Then: "You got along pretty good, did you?"

"Oh, yes. But we didn't see much of each other. Her hours at the hospital—"

"What hospital?"

"GWU. I mean, the George Washington University—"

"Did she have a boy friend?"

"I don't know. No one ever came here. She went out sometimes.

Dressed for a date. But not so often, considering how pretty she was." A quick flash of a crumpled body, red smeared face, empty eyes.

"Stay out all night? Go away for weekends?"

Quinn shook her head.

"She never talked about a man? Somebody she was crazy about that she couldn't have? A married doctor, maybe?"

"It wasn't that way between us. We just lived together. As I said, sharing the rent."

But there might have been more. If there'd been time. Quinn shook under the assault of sudden memory. Jenny had suggested lunch on a Saturday afternoon. Once she'd talked of a picnic on the canal towpath. Quinn had made excuses, retreating. There had been three apartment mates before. It was useless to make friends and lose them. But Jenny persisted. They'd gone out together a few times, and it was fun. Then one night over late coffee, Quinn had heard herself speaking about her parents. Jenny had listened, said nothing. But later, when they were in their beds, she had whispered, "It's nice you have good memories."

Johnson was asking, "Could she have been in trouble?" A pause. "Did she take drugs?"

"No trouble," Quinn said softly. "And no, she didn't take drugs. She didn't even smoke cigarettes."

"Her health?"

"She'd have to be strong to be a nurse, wouldn't she?"

Jason made a soft "Um," and Johnson glanced at him, but said to Quinn, "What about her family, Miss Monroe? We need a next of kin to notify."

"She never mentioned anybody." Not the night Quinn had spoken of her own people. Not later.

"But we all have somebody," Johnson protested.

Not me, Quinn thought. I don't.

"And after the autopsy . . ."

Jenny had to be buried. That's what the detective was saying. Quinn thought of her savings. She had seven hundred dollars, but funerals were expensive. Maybe she could borrow the rest. She'd have to. It was all she could do for Jenny now. She choked out, "I'll take care of it myself."

Johnson seemed not to hear. "What about letters? Phone calls."

"Bills," Quinn said. "From Saks, Lord & Taylor. She only made local calls, and I don't know to whom."

"We have to look through her things." Johnson was apologetic. "In case there's an address for her folks. A letter tucked away."

Quinn struggled to her feet. She led the two men to the gold-and-brown bedroom, indicated the chest that had been Jenny's, pushed back the sliding door of the closet, and waved to the left. "Hers."

Hands folded together, Quinn waited while Jason made a careful search, until, at the top drawer, he said, "Johnson, look here," and held out a ring. "And at this," and offered a pair of earclips.

Johnson frowned. "Real?"

"Um," Jason agreed.

"Pretty expensive for a nurse," Johnson said, raising his brows at Quinn. "Real diamonds. Where do you suppose she got them?"

"Real *diamonds?*" Quinn whispered.

"I guess you don't know," Johnson said sadly. "The way you people live . . . I don't get it."

Quinn didn't know how to explain. People roomed together, spoke of clothes, costs, jobs; brushed shoulders but not hearts. There was a little while of knowing, and then time would intervene, and everything would disappear. That was how it was. For everybody. But the flickering memories returned. Jenny asking, "How about it, Quinn? Want to go to Woodie's with me?" Sometimes Quinn agreed; sometimes not. If she had said yes more often, would Jenny have come to trust her enough to talk of what was wrong? If there'd been more time, could Quinn have learned to be the friend that Jenny had needed? Now Quinn would never know.

"What should I do?" she asked the detective.

"Have supper. Go to sleep. Get up tomorrow and go to work," Johnson answered.

Moments after the police left, Lew Selby phoned. She frowned when she heard his "Quinn, I just heard it on the news. I'm sorry about Jenny. I'll be over in a little while."

"No," she told him. "I'm all right." She put the phone down on his aggrieved protest.

She had broken the affair off a month before because he'd begun to bore her, just as her job had begun to bore her lately. He kept calling her, wanting to start again. She wasn't having any.

She bedded down on the sofa that night, falling in and out of fitful dreams while the lights of the Geico building three blocks away made patterns on the ceiling.

Two days later, Johnson and Jason were back. "She had family," Johnson told Quinn. "Here's the address. We've notified them."

"Parents?" Quinn asked, bewildered. "People she never mentioned?"

"Mother and father," Johnson said. "Not that they were easy to find. The hospital records here didn't list them on her employment sheet. She left out answers to those questions, and I guess nobody noticed. Same thing at the Chicago nursing school. Except they had college transcripts. The college had an old address. We put in a call. Her folks hadn't heard from her in something like seven years."

"But why?" Jenny had said it was nice that Quinn had good things to remember. This must have meant that Jenny didn't.

"She disappeared after she got her two-year certificate from school. They didn't say any more about it."

Quinn felt wrapped in sudden chill. She had lived five months with Jenny and never known that her smiling face was a mask that hid— hid what?

"About her things," Johnson said.

"I'll send them."

"Put plenty of insurance on that jewelry."

Within two days Quinn had written a note explaining who she was and offering condolences and slipped it into one of the packages she mailed to the Lakas family. The return receipts came back. She waited hopefully. But there was nothing more. Except for the constant memory of Jenny . . .

CHAPTER 3

Sound and light exploded at the same time, assaulting Quinn with bomblike concussions. She jerked her head in reflex as time resumed its normal course. A throb of pain brought her upright, brushing her hair from her eyes.

The blasting horn and blazing high beams were gone. The Old North Road was still and dark and empty once again. A pale blur in the heavy clouds marked Elkhorn's center, two miles away. Cory's Wine and Liquors. The Rolls-Royce dealership. The Burger Barn. Fieldstone's Market. Sears' garage. And, further on, the State Police substation.

Six hundred and twenty-some miles from the suburbs of Washington. A small town called Elkhorn. That's where she was. She slapped the steering wheel angrily, and said aloud, "No more. It's done."

There had been those sleepless weeks when she asked herself how she might have helped, why she hadn't been a better friend to Jenny. Those days of wondering what Jenny's mask had hidden; why she had died. The job seemed more deadly boring than ever. Lew Selby continued to pursue. The city was hot and uncivil. The job had been boring before. Lew had pursued her before. But Jenny's suicide was the last straw.

When Irene mentioned her cousin Helen Martenson, who lived in a small New England town and took in boarders, Quinn immediately wrote to her, knowing it was time to take a positive step into the future. A month later, her belongings stored, she flew to Boston, and there took a plane for the twenty-five-minute trip to Passamody. Helen met her, drove her the eight miles to Elkhorn. She smiled when she saw the snowy meadows, the stand of silver birches near the lane.

But the past had reached for her on the Old North Road.

"No more," she said again, taking the flashlight from the glove compartment.

She climbed stiffly from the car, stamped to the highway.

Somewhere behind her an unidentified thing had lunged at her. It might have been a deer, even a man. And it might have been the memory of Jenny Lakas.

Having trudged back the way she had come, Quinn stopped at the bend of a curve. A glimmer of white tilted at her. She knew it at once, and kicked through knee-high snow to thrust upright the canted sign.

She turned her light on it, and read JESUS SAVES. The work of an amateur, with the first two letters big and strong and the rest of them tiny, cramped to fit the space, and paler, too, as if the painter had lost his zeal while he labored.

She was unaware of the snow melting over her boot tops. She didn't feel the chill on her cheeks, nor the bruise that spread between her brows. She stood bemused by instant understanding.

A little while before Helen had reminded her of Jenny. And just now, passing the sign, she must have caught a glimpse of the first two large letters. JE. For Jenny. That had been enough to pitch her back through time and miles.

She turned briskly from the sign, and from the recognition. She wouldn't think of Jenny anymore.

She was cold, bruised, and very angry. The moment's inattention to driving that had caused the skid had been a sign of weakness. And weakness was the danger.

She returned to where the Rabbit had settled like a tired animal. Jerking the keys from the ignition, she unlocked the hatchback and pushed aside sample cases and the other paraphernalia of her job. As a district manager for Becker's, a nationwide cosmetics firm, she carried most of her office with her.

The flares she lit glowed with a purple-pink light that reminded her of the Fourth of July fire fountains she had burned on the front lawn as a child, her mother nervously watching while her father murmured reassurance from the hammock.

Quinn told herself she would forget that, too, and slammed the hatch lid with a satisfying thud.

The immediate goal was to see if the Rabbit was undamaged and safe to drive. By Monday it had to be ready to go. She wasn't about to allow a moment's foolish weakness to affect her job. She had ads in Sunday's help wanteds in Riverton and St. Mary's City. Girls would be coming for interviews. If the car was okay now, she would go on to Cory's and buy the Marsala. If not, she must know it.

Flashlight in hand, she got down between the two front wheels. The beam slipped, flickered. She acknowledged the hand tremor with an irritated curse, but twisted her head to study the bottom of the car. With the small movement some protruding part dragged off her cap. Long hair tumbled down again. She blew it from before her eyes, squinted upward.

No stain of oil. No ominous hanging parts. Good. But not so good was the ridge of ice crushed against the undercarriage at the universal joint. She pressed it hard with stiff fingers. It was solid.

Cold seeped from the snow beneath her into her belly. The bruise throbbed insistently. She tried to decide if she dare move the Rabbit off the snowbank, assuming that she could.

There was a sudden glow of headlights, the crunch of wheels cut off the road and on to the snowy shoulder. A door slammed. Footsteps approached.

A deep male voice called, "Hey, do you need any help?"

"No, thanks," she said. "I can manage."

There was a brief silence while Michael Dayman considered. The jeans, the boots, the long legs sprawling between the wheels had seemed to belong to a teenaged boy. The voice that had responded to his question didn't belong to a boy, teenage or otherwise. It was husky, though edged with briskness. He said, "I think maybe you'd better let me have a look."

Quinn inched backward, her weight on her elbows and knees, catching her cap as she went. Clear of the wheels, she rose. With the flash in one hand, the cap in the other, she said to the tall blurred figure that loomed over her, "Thank you for stopping. I guess I can't manage after all. I'm afraid the Rabbit's hung up."

Michael didn't answer at once. In the moment's silence that followed, she stared at him. Very tall. And burly in the dark heavy car coat. His face lean, though. His eyes unreadable in the shadows.

He looked at her and saw the red-gold hair that seemed freshly minted, and a willowy slimness only emphasized by parka with jeans. He took the flash from her, beamed it off to the side so that her face was bathed in its indirect light.

Her eyes were black, but flecked with gray. They peered at him steadily, then narrowed. There was a dusting of freckles on her nose. A firm mouth that might show humor. Now it was beginning to tighten with impatience. He saw the bruise on her forehead, stepped closer. "Are you hurt?"

"It's nothing. I banged my head when I skidded."

"You're sure you're okay?" It was her expression that made him wonder. She had a look of shock. Or maybe it was just the bitter cold. "Warm up in my car."

"There's no need."

The impatience was in her voice as well as her eyes. It reminded him how much he disliked independent women. He said, "Have it your way. I'll take a look." A moment later, rising from a crouch, he said, "It does seem stuck. But have you tried to move it?"

"I'm worried about damaging the oil pan."

Michael shrugged. "I don't know where the oil pan is. Leave your car until morning when it thaws. I'll drive you wherever you want to go."

"It's going to snow tonight. Which means tomorrow will be worse." She went to the hatch. He followed, beamed the light, and she opened it again. "If we lighten the load it could make the difference." She leaned to take out a heavy carton.

"I'll do that," he protested. He shoved the torch into her hand.

But she wedged the light in a corner of the hatch, and worked with him. Bathed in the purple pink of the flares, they quickly emptied it.

Once more he went down to hands and knees at the front end. Now he could see the edge of the groove cut into the ice. There was still no clearance, however. He got a shovel from his car, slid beneath the Rabbit. A few quick clattering blows. In a little while, he rose. "Let's see if that's done it. Want me to try?"

But she got behind the wheel. She had tucked her hair under her cap again. It seemed to Michael that its glow had noticeably gone from the dark.

She put the key in the ignition, turned the switch. Nothing happened. Her lips moved in what could only have been a silent curse.

Reaching through the window, he shoved the automatic gear shift into park position. "How about now?"

She grinned. "I forgot it stalled." When she tried that time, the motor caught. She eased the car off the ice ridge to the shoulder and stopped. Together they reloaded the hatch, extinguished the flares.

When she was ready to drive away, she thanked him and got behind the wheel.

Reluctant to let her go, he leaned both hands on the window edge. "Take it easy."

"I'll head straight for Bill Sears' garage."

He didn't know her name, or where she lived, and though Elkhorn was a small town, it was spread out. He said, "I'll be right behind you."

"Don't bother." But she was aware of a quickening between them, and a hum within herself, as if something long dormant were beginning to come alive. And, as she inched carefully across the shoulder to the highway, his lights flashed on behind her and moved with her, combining with her own to make a comfortable tunnel through the cave of the dark. When she saw the neon of the Sears' sign, she rolled the window down, waved her thanks, and turned in. Michael followed.

She saw that Bill Sears, the garage owner and chief mechanic, was shoulder-deep in an engine. Shivering, she turned to Michael, who had come to stand beside her. "He's busy. You might as well go on. I'll call someone to pick me up."

"But I'm already here," Michael answered, wondering who that someone was.

Bill Sears approached, greeted Michael, raised his left earflap, and asked Quinn what the trouble was. She explained. He said, "Have to get it on the hoist. Can't until tomorrow."

Quinn gave him the keys, started toward the telephone booth, intending to call Helen to meet her at Cory's across the road.

But Michael insisted that he would drive her. When she explained about the wine, he said he could manage that, too.

He drove her to Cory's, went inside with her. In the bright warmth, she saw that his eyes were a clear blue in his tanned face, and that the hair ruffled across his brow was very dark. While she bought the Marsala, he pulled out a dollar for a lottery ticket.

"How about it?" he grinned. "Want to try your luck?"

She was ready to be diverted. She bought a dollar ticket in the weekly draw. She thrust it into her jeans, suddenly feeling foolish. She had never won anything and didn't expect to now.

But Michael wanted to see it. When she showed it to him, he read off the numbers. "Red 01 Green 33 Blue 19. A nice combination."

He shrugged at his loss on the instant payoff game. "My contribution to the state's economy."

Outside there was the first gentle sift of snow on the wind. She shivered and clutched the wine, remembering the JESUS SAVES sign, the wild skid through the night, the frightening backward spin of time.

Michael said, "Look, do you mind if I stop at my place for a minute before I take you home? I've got to pick up a letter to get into the mail this evening."

"Of course," she said. "I'm not in a hurry.

Even as they exchanged names, he knew that to him this was to be something more than a onetime chance encounter. She was the first girl to interest him seriously since he'd left Katherine a year before. He forgot the brief familiar bitterness as he smiled at Quinn.

He helped her into the car, got in himself. The windshield wipers clicked gently, stroking away a drift of snow. He paused at the edge of the drive to allow a fuel truck to rumble by, its cab and body aglow with red and green lights. When it had disappeared beyond the Burger Barn, he eased into the empty road.

Within moments they had sketched brief biographies for each other. She told him that she had been born in Richmond, Virginia, had lived there until she went to college. Most recently she had worked in Washington, D.C. He told her that he knew Washington well, having gone there from Boston many times in connection with his job. He worked on a Boston newspaper, but had returned to Elkhorn, his hometown, on a year's leave to do a book. He didn't mention his Pulitzer prize, nor the five years of his marriage to Katherine.

Quinn felt the hum of expectation in her grow stronger. She hadn't gone out with a man since the move to Elkhorn. There had been only a few men in her life before. Chuck Ford in college. A promising first affair that ended in the shock and aftermath pain of her parents' death. That memory still hurt. Then, in Washington, there had been Neil, who drifted off. She hadn't minded. And Lew Selby, who'd gotten too serious to enjoy.

Looking at Michael's profile, his strong chin, his long straight nose, she was glad that she had met him on this particular evening.

A short distance past the State Police substation, they turned right into a narrow graveled road. A house suddenly appeared before them, its dusting of snow agleam in the headlights, but shadowed by the heavy drooping arms of tall shaggy spruce that shut away the sky.

He left the motor running, got out. "It'll only take a minute." But when he reached the steps, he stopped, returned. "You still look half frozen. Come in and warm up on a drink." He was thirty-five years old, well traveled, and successful, but in that moment he felt like an adolescent, and was ruefully aware that he sounded like one, too.

Outside the car, she stopped to listen. Over the wind, she heard the deep rhythmic boom of the ocean.

"You're close to shore," she said.

"Yes. But it's a climb down a cliff, impossible now with the icy rock. I'll take you when spring comes."

"Spring seems far away." She smiled. "Who knows where we'll be by then?"

"Here," he answered. And added: "I hope." When she didn't reply, he unlocked the door.

Inside, he grinned, turned on a lamp. "Bachelor's quarters. I'll clean it up someday."

She looked around.

It was a long room with a fireplace at one end, and wide double doors that opened into a sleeping porch, also used as a den, to judge by desk and typewriter and file cabinets.

The rug was a faded Oriental, with a beautiful silken sheen. The furniture was low and soft. Crowded bookshelves lined the walls.

"Nice," she said at last. And: "This house has been loved."

"Yes, it has been. My folks built it, lived here all their lives. I was born here."

"It sounds so—so permanent."

"It was. Still is." He already had the feeling that she belonged there.

He took her chin in his hand, tipped her face up, and touched the bruise on her forehead gently. "This all right?" When she nodded, he said, "Then get out of your boots and wet parka."

He built a fire quickly, disappeared down the hall toward what she supposed was the kitchen. Soon he returned with two large mugs.

She sniffed appreciatively at the aroma of strong coffee and good brandy.

"Warming up now?" he asked.

She nodded. "I ought to phone."

He waved toward the den. "Help yourself. You'll find it somewhere on the desk under that mound of papers."

It took only a moment to tell Helen about the Rabbit, to suggest that she not wait dinner.

That done, Quinn returned to the sofa, took up her mug, and leaned back contentedly. From outside she could still hear the boom of the ocean, the hiss of falling snow. She looked into the leaping flames. Earlier, she had felt the shadows of the past reach out to her. They were gone now.

She smiled. "I'm glad you suggested this."

"I am, too. It can be frightening to almost have an accident." A faint question in his voice.

"Yes." The memory of terror returned. Jenny's flaccid hand, clouded eyes . . . "But it was my own fault. I wasn't paying attention."

"So it came like an ambush out of the dark."

She gave him a long steady look. "You sound as if you know."

"I do know," he said soberly. He thought of a dim winding track in Vietnam. He had turned his head to glance at a fiery sunset. The soldier moving before him stepped on a land mine . . . bright air broke and quivered . . . Michael didn't speak of it.

She saw the remembering in his eyes, and curled her hand in his, shifting closer, so they pressed shoulder to shoulder in sudden urgency.

He took her into his arms, his mouth finding her lips, whispering "Quinn, Quinn," against them. She clung to him with a quick answering eagerness.

Together they rose, moved to the bed in the sleeping porch.

A rustle of shaggy spruce limbs against the window. A whisper of snow. A brief separation, and the sounds of buttons and snaps and zippers, as clothing came off and fell away.

Then she was back in his arms, responding to his lean strength with passionate hunger. He caressed her, her breasts and thighs, while she held her lips to his, as if breathing with him.

Their coming together was easy and natural, a joining of mutual hungers, of bodies that seemed already to know each other, but with no words spoken, no promises offered or given. They rode currents that carried them to a high hot cresting, then, without breath, they fell back, still clinging to each other.

Snuggled against him, her cheek turned to the warmth of his chest, she drowsed. She heard the beat of his heart in syncopation with the distant muted boom of the ocean.

Later, stirring, he spread his fingers on the curve of her hip. "I thought you were skinny. But there's plenty to get hold of."

She looked up at him through her lashes. "Or else you have big hands."

"We both get credit." Then, in gladness and gratitude: "It was good, Quinn."

She drew away, stretched languidly. "Time to go, Michael."

"Stay. We'll have something to eat. We can see about your car in the morning."

She shook her head.

"You can call home again, you know."

She laughed. "Of course I can."

"Then why not?"

She shrugged, sat up, reaching for her clothes.

"How about supper? You must be starved. I am." When she nodded, he rose. He pulled on trousers, and brought her a robe that obviously was his.

She tried to take it, but he helped her into it, rolled the too-long sleeves into neat cuffs, then held her tightly to him.

"Thank you," she said, and touched his cheek. "Thank you for everything, Michael."

"It's just the beginning," he told her, and felt her slight withdrawal. His hands came up to cup her cheeks gently. "It's not just talk, Quinn. You'll see."

She said in a low, frightened voice, "I wouldn't want you to misunderstand this. You mustn't have the wrong idea. Don't think that it —that this means anything."

"Doesn't it?"

"No," she whispered. "No, of course not. How could it?"

"It could, and does, and will. I'll make it mean something," he told her.

"No," she said again. "Don't you see? It was just something nice that happened. That we both wanted, and needed tonight. It's done now."

He knew he wasn't going to let their meeting go at that. It meant everything. Both to him and to her. He'd have to teach her that. But he sensed her fear. No need to hurry. There was time. He grinned. "My dear girl, if you only knew how you sound. Very much like a married man who has seduced his secretary and is scared that he's made a commitment that's going to give him trouble."

"Be serious," she said, faintly pink in her cheeks.

"I am. Or let's say I'm trying to be, though it isn't exactly easy, since it seems to me that I only hinted I intend to see you again."

But there had been more. She had known it, tried to warn him. She said, "I wanted to be honest with you."

"I know." He patted her head. "Come on. Let's go get the steaks."

CHAPTER 4

A stand of birches ghostly in morning light. Beyond, the gleam of fresh snow. Then home. The glow at the windows warm and welcoming.

Helen was back before Quinn, having dropped her off to pick up the Rabbit.

She stopped on the threshold. The good silence. That was Elkhorn.

Washington had been hard hating eyes glimpsed briefly on buses, a dull office job that confined her indoors, Lew Selby's useless entreaties. And at the last, blue blinking domes and wailing sirens. And Jenny.

Quinn missed nothing of what she had left behind.

At her feet there rose a deep purr. Huge emerald eyes shone at her. She swooped to pick up the kitten. "You can't go out, Devil. It's too cold."

Devil was all black, with a sharp triangular face and tiny ears. He had appeared one evening from under Quinn's car at the Inland Motel in Windsor. She had fed him milk and found him on her doorstep the next morning. He followed her to the Rabbit, and yowled as she drove off. On her return a week later, he trotted out to greet her. "You devil. What are you still doing here?" she said. He wrapped himself around her legs and clawed her boots. She took him with her when she left.

Now she cuddled him under her arm and closed the door behind her.

"The car's really okay?" Helen asked.

"No trouble. Thanks for the lift to Sears'."

"Thanks! Good heavens, Quinn. It was nothing."

"Sorry about your veal Marsala. I'll do it next weekend instead."

"If you like." Then: "But I was uneasy last night. When you finally called, I was sure it was bad news."

Bad news. The old resonance shook Quinn. She said, "You shouldn't have worried," and escaped to her room.

She curled on the padded window seat, looking at the old house that lay below the crest of the hill beyond the snow-covered meadows. Vacant for years, it had once belonged to Helen's family, but had been sold generations back, and then lost to the state for non-payment of taxes. Quinn had often thought of exploring it, but now it became a distant blur . . .

She was in class. A student slipped in with a whisper of hurried footsteps. The instructor glanced at a note. "Miss Monroe, this is for you."

In moments she was on the steps of the Administration Building. A crowd of demonstrators. Their strident shouts were background to her silent scream of fear. Then the dean's office. Her hand shook as she held the phone.

Her father said, panting, "Quinn, it's bad news. Your mother's had another heart attack. You'd better come."

She spent a short time looking for Chuck Ford, but couldn't find him. So she set out alone. Four hours later she was in the lobby of Ridgefield Hospital. She asked at the desk. The clerk gave her an odd look. "I'll find out." Within moments the elevator door opened. A strange physician stepped out, came to her. "Miss Monroe?"

"Where's my dad? How's my mom?"

The physician answered, "It's bad news."

Her mother had collapsed over bridge, been rushed to the hospital. Quinn's father was at the office. He had apparently telephoned Quinn and started for Ridgefield by cab, fearing to drive himself. On arrival, the driver found him unconscious on the back seat. He died at the threshold of the emergency room.

Quinn was just barely eighteen then. She had no brothers or sisters, no aunts or uncles. No one to turn to. She managed alone, shocked into numbness. When she returned to college she was a different girl from the one she had been. She tried but the numbness enveloped her. Gaiety was gone, and with it laughter.

Her sorority sisters, at first sympathetic, began to shy away from her.

Chuck pretended for a little while, then became impatient. "You're always drooping around, Quinn. Come on. Shake it." And, finally sullen: "You aren't fun anymore. And you get me broody, too. So I guess that's it."

She taught herself to accept and value her loneliness and call it freedom. Friendship, even love, always ended, and ended in pain. She didn't want any more.

She finished two years of college on money from the sale of the house, lived on her father's insurance. When it was down to seven hundred dollars, she moved to Washington and found a job. Time passed. She was busy with her life. The memory of loss remained fresh. But she wouldn't give in to it . . .

As she blinked back tears, something glittered near the eaves of the old house across the meadow. Bright sun flashed on the snow fields. She turned away, suddenly thinking of Michael.

It was late afternoon. She sat near the stove, the Sunday papers spread on her knees. Devil chewed the laces of her sneakers. Her green sweater was laddered at both elbows, and the jeans patched. She hadn't creamed her face, nor made up, nor done her hair. Saturdays and Sundays were hers.

At the ring of the bell, Helen visibly brightened. When she opened the door, Michael asked for Quinn.

She craned her neck to see past Helen's blocking body as the older woman, brightening even more, asked him in.

He smiled at Helen, saluted Quinn.

He was taller than she remembered. His eyes were even bluer.

There was a leap of peculiar current between them. As if two separate fires had jumped in a gust of air and arced together.

She broke it by introducing him to Helen. He asked if Quinn would drive to Passamody with him. She agreed, and while he and Helen chatted, she went to change.

They reached Passamody at twilight. It was the largest city in the south of the state, a deepwater port from which whaling ships had once sailed. The old section ringed the harbor, part slum and part restored, with a few boutiques, a bookstore, and a paint-supply shop in premises once filled by ships' chandlers and fishermen's huts.

Quinn and Michael window-shopped as they walked to the movie house, talking about her travels in the area. He found her observant, with something to say about each of the towns she knew. It was only when he asked about her time in Washington that she seemed to withdraw.

After the movie, they stopped at a café for pizza. The jukebox thundered rock 'n' roll. They gave up conversation.

They drove through hushed twilight back to Elkhorn.

When he slowed at the turn to his house, she put her hand on his. "Michael. No."

He pulled over, jammed on the brake, and turned to her. "Why not?"

"I told you," she said. "I didn't want you to—"

He grinned, shook his head. "Stop it, Quinn."

"There's no reason to make a habit—"

"Some habits are good."

She said slowly, "Even the ones that are good hurt when you have to break them."

He gave her a long silent look, then cut back to the highway. Within moments he pulled into Old Barn Road.

She said, "I'm sorry, Michael."

"For what?"

"You know."

"But I don't. Spell it out for me. Are you sorry because you didn't *want* to stop at my place? Or sorry I didn't argue more?"

A silent moment of debate. Then: "I don't know."

He parked before the house. "I'm a very bullheaded man."

"I begin to see that." And soberly: "That's not always helpful."

"Which remains to be seen."

He watched as she went inside, unwilling to see her go, and wondering at himself. She had nothing of the sweet sexy cuddly quality that Katherine had had when he first met her. Yet he wanted her as he had wanted to other woman since his return to Elkhorn when his marriage to Katherine broke up.

It had started out good, but had gone bad quickly. The year was 1971. He'd just come back from Vietnam. He'd had a surfeit of body counts, mass graves, and napalmed rice fields. He was sick to his heart at what he had seen and written about in the dispatches sent to the Boston newspaper for which he worked. He came home in despair, and in need to begin again to believe in life. He and Katherine met at the paper. Every man in the place had tried to get her. She was cute, round-faced, and responsive. Michael felt lucky when she agreed to marry him.

A few months later, he won the Pulitzer prize for the sweat and pain he had poured into his Vietnam stories. The money wasn't all that much, but the award gave him a name. He had his pick of jobs. He stayed on in Boston, flew to Washington, San Francisco and Houston as work demanded, and happily returned to the three-story townhouse he had bought. For a while, Katherine basked in shared importance. But after a year she began to complain that she never saw him. She wanted a nine-to-five husband, who could go to consciousness-raising sessions with her, and body-language meetings. He couldn't, and wouldn't. Very soon he realized that she believed in every commercial she heard on television, every ad she read in the magazines. She filled their home with gadgets. She had a spell of wearing tarty clothes, another of dressing like a prim schoolteacher.

He came home one night, found the apartment empty. Returning late, she was high enough on something not to tiptoe or whisper. The next morning she carefully detailed the meeting she had attended. Within a month she had gone political, and shifted to a different group. A few weeks later she was striking a match on the bottom of her jeans, and calling him a male chauvinist pig, and refusing to cook or take his shirts to the laundry. She took a course in mechanics, and served him carburetors and lug wrenches with the pickup meals he had prepared. She disappeared for a weekend to join a demonstration in front of the White House. She had gone to New Hampshire with the Clamshell Alliance.

He tried to follow the twists and turns of her new vocabulary, but to him it seemed as if liberation was always the word, always that, and never love. When she moved his dresser into the living room and made up his bed on the sofa, he said he wasn't having any more.

Laughing, she told him to go fuck himself.

He walked out on her, the house, and their joint bank account. Two weeks after their divorce became final, he saw her smiling prettily into the face of a short, full-faced man with muttonchop sideburns. She wore a flowered chiffon gown and pearls at her throat. Michael arranged a year's leave of absence and returned to Elkhorn to work on a book about what had happened in the United States to the refugees from Vietnam. He lived, breathed, drowned himself in their stories until the night before.

Now a light came on in Quinn's window. A slim silhouette appeared. As he started for home he wondered how soon he could see her again.

Quinn arrived in Riverton on Tuesday in late afternoon after a grueling drive on the unplowed All-State. She checked into the Blue Bell, where she always stayed, and immediately took a hot shower to chase the chill from her bones. She was drying herself when the phone rang in her room.

It was Michael saying, "Hi, Quinn. I'm downstairs. Want to come and have a drink with me?"

"But how did you know—"

"Helen told me. Can you come down?"

"It'll be a few minutes."

Soon he watched her approach. No man could ever mistake her for a teenage boy now. Her hair was drawn back, sleeked into shining curls on the nape of her neck. Her brows were dark and straight over the gray-flecked pools of her dark tilted eyes. Elegant in her black silk suit, made up and perfumed, she was luminously beautiful. He was speechless as she came toward him.

She smiled into his astonished face. "What's the matter?"

"I almost didn't know you."

"You see before you me in my working clothes. I can't play district manager in jeans."

"I don't believe it. It's like Dr. Jekyll and Mr. Hyde."

"I hope not," she laughed.

They had a drink apiece, and then they had dinner together. After two dances in the lounge, Quinn made a great show of yawning. Michael insisted on a nightcap, and walked her back to her room.

He didn't ask if he could go in with her. It didn't occur to him. He bent to kiss her good-night, and they were inside together. She was in his arms, willing, loving, all that he needed. That was all that he cared about then.

It snowed on Friday. Quinn was late. It was dark when she drove through the opening in the stone wall. As she recognized Michael's car, a small wave of heat rippled through her.

She stepped from the Rabbit on to a small shoveled place. The black kitten Devil offered his usual greeting and caress. Light spilled into the yard as the door opened and Michael came to her. She saw the look of suppressed excitement on his face, and felt a similar stir within herself.

"Come on in," he told her. "I'll help you unload later."

When she had taken off her coat and hat, had pulled off her boots, he asked casually, "Listen, Quinn, do you have your lottery ticket handy?"

"It's around somewhere, I guess." She could hear Helen moving in the kitchen, and started to go in to say hello.

But Michael said, "Wait," and she turned back to him. "Find your ticket. Now."

"But what's going on?"

"Do what I say."

She went slowly up the steps to her room. The ticket was crumpled into her jeans, where she had left it the Friday before.

Helen was at the kitchen door when she returned to the living area. Quinn paused to greet her.

Helen nodded but was silent, her face alight with expectation.

Michael took the bit of cardboard from Quinn, glanced at it, then drew from his pocket a torn-away section of a newspaper page. He compared the two. "Red 01 Green 33 Blue 19—I thought I remembered." And, with a whoop of laughter: "Quinn, you've won!"

Helen shrieked.

But Quinn was bewildered. "What are you talking about, Michael?"

"The weekly draw, my girl. You've taken it. One hundred thousand dollars' worth of prize money."

"Me?" she asked tremulously.

"You."

She frowned, rejecting, disbelieving.

Around her, the excitement rose up in quick currents. Helen chattering. Michael laughing. Even Devil clawing the sofa.

Quinn felt as if she were drowning in their joy. The blood drained from her face, the air from her lungs.

Michael saw. He eased her into a chair. "It's okay. Catch your breath and let it sink in."

Helen was saying, "The old house . . . a few thousand to do a new kitchen. Another few for the baths. A studio with a north window . . ."

Quinn whispered, "I don't believe it, Michael. It can't be true."

But he showed her that the two numbers matched. Slowly the truth became obvious. With the first lottery ticket she had ever bought, she had won the weekly draw.

Her face flushed. Visions danced before her sparkling eyes. A full moon hanging over the Egyptian pyramids . . . The winding lanes of Marrakesh . . . A globe of the world spun beneath her father's fingers. She threw back her head, laughing. "I know what I'm going to do." She jumped to her feet, flung her arms around Michael. "It's what I've always dreamed of. And now I can make it true!"

He hugged her to him, while Helen murmured sadly about the old house.

There had not been much else in the way of dramatic happenings that particular weekend. The article and picture distributed by the State Lottery Commission were picked up by the Associated Press within hours and reprinted throughout the country the next day.

The following week, the first of the letters came.

CHAPTER 5

The letter was the fourth one that Quinn opened. It was in a plain white envelope and had no return address. Its smeared postmark was from Kansas City, Missouri. It said, *You're one of the few chosen. Do you know how lucky you are? I write to tell you that I'm happy for you in your good fortune. You're lucky to be young and beautiful and rich and ALIVE. Enjoy it while you can.* It was signed, *A Friend.*

When Helen asked about the mail, Quinn told her it was all junk, and threw it away. She kept the unsigned letter, without knowing why. She didn't mention it to Helen, nor did she tell Michael about it when he stopped by the next day, although by then she had received another one.

The mailbox had been full that Saturday morning. But the plain white envelope caught her eye at once. Her hand shook as she turned it over. No return address. A Kansas City postmark again.

She read the message quickly. *It's wonderful to be a winner. I hope you appreciate your good fortune. Some people are born with it, and some are not. Enjoy being ALIVE.*

Her toes became ice cubes inside her new Gucci boots. Her body was frozen within the mink coat she had bought in Boston two days before.

She took the letter indoors, along with the other mail, where Devil purred for attention. She rubbed his sleek head absently, then went to throw all but the one thing away. Once again she told no one about it. She saved it with the first she had received, and tried not to think of them. But she did occasionally through the weekend, and when that happened, she went queasy with something akin to embarrassment, something too close to fear.

That was when she remembered how it had all begun in the first week of February, with an inconsequential conversation, a radio newscast, and an empty bottle of wine.

But by that Monday the excitement was largely over. She had been a seven-day wonder. Now there were new wonders to come.

At seven in the morning, she was in Passamody. She went to the post office as usual, picked up an armload of travel folders at the airport, stopped to buy a comic valentine to send to Michael, and set out for Riverton in high spirits.

The setting sun was a blinding red glare at the edge of Kenyon, Kansas. Long dark shadows reached down the chilled streets.

Jerry Lakas moved in and out of them. It was like going from day to night to day. But with no bad dreams between. He had a bundle of newspapers under his arm, and was hurrying back to the house to read them while he had his supper. Two *New York Times,* a *Boston Globe,* a tattered *Washington Post.* He was certain that somewhere, if he looked carefully, he'd find her name in one of them. He'd know what had happened.

Since that first small article, he'd been hoping for more, waiting for more. He wanted to know what she was doing and thinking and feeling. But he'd been unable to find another mention of her in the *Star.* So he'd arranged to have these other papers delivered for him to the bus terminal.

As he reached the house a black cat ran in front of him. He stopped. The cold became fire on his skin. He was locked where he stood. It was just crazy superstition. But he was scared. He drew a deep breath.

"Scaredy cat!" Jenny whispered in his ear. Breath warm and sweet. "Four years older than me, and such a baby scaredy cat!" Her voice belonged to a girl of six, but it was ageless, too; the voice of the temptress hiding inside every woman's body. He felt her hot wet tongue lick the palm of his hand, the sharp dainty nibble of her tiny teeth. Need was pain in his blood and flesh.

He turned quickly and, avoiding the path of the cat, walked around the side of the house through the deep snow. He stamped it off before he went in the back door.

His mother turned from the stove. "You're late, Jerry."

He nodded, didn't answer. The smell of old body was in his nostrils. He put the newspaper bundle on the table near his plate. He put the transistor radio next to it.

"What's that?" she asked.

He took off his coat, hung it on a hook behind the door. He sat down at the table. He listened to her sigh as he switched the radio on, to the clatter of the soup ladle in the pot. The smell of old body choked him. But when she had put the steaming bowl before him he said, "Newspapers."

"Looks like a lot of them."

He ate silently. Lima beans, snap beans, okra. Jenny hated okra. He pushed the bowl aside.

"Want more, Jerry?"

He shook his head.

His mother replaced the half-empty bowl with a plate. Pork chops. A baked sweet potato. He ate quickly now, reaching with one hand for a paper, but letting it go when his mother said tentatively, "Your pa's going to be waiting. He's hungry, too."

It could hold a little longer. Jerry listened to the songs and announcements that came from the transistor radio while he finished his meal. With his coat on, he took the newspapers under his arm. He could leave them, though he knew she would turn the pages curiously as soon as he had gone. It didn't matter if she snooped. She didn't know anything about it. She hadn't seen the small article that mentioned tall beautiful Quinn Monroe.

His father was at the door when he returned to the pharmacy. Coat and hat on, unbuckled boots flapping on his feet. He grunted a sour "I'll be back soon," and left Jerry alone.

He leaned against the counter, the old smell of his father still surrounding him. He ignored it. It would soon go away.

He was a man of thirty-three, with chestnut hair cropped short, and sleepy gray eyes. He switched on the transistor, then stared blindly past the day-old Valentine's Day candy display on the crowded shelves on the opposite wall.

It was an old-fashioned place. Open 8 A.M. until 9 P.M. The soda fountain was gone, though. It had disappeared, along with the young people who used to crowd the stools. Jenny at the center of them. He, outside always, watching.

He pulled the newspaper toward him. He read slowly, saying the words in his mind. He stopped once to point out the public phone booth behind the magazine rack, once to sell a bottle of liniment. He put the exact sum into the cash register. He hadn't taken in enough that day to be able to get away with keeping it for himself. But, thinking of his Kansas City bank account, he grinned. There was enough for whatever he wanted. It had always been that way. Enough for what Jenny wanted, too. Even when she'd say, "Jerry, you don't belong here. Go home," she'd accepted twenty dollars for a new red skirt. She'd let him buy her the red cheerleader outfit she needed. With that in mind, he returned to his reading. He went through the papers twice.

Nothing. He stared blankly at the wall again. There had to be more. He had written as soon as he saw the article. Then he had written again. It wasn't enough. He glanced quickly at the door, then went to the stationery shelf and got paper and an envelope. He took his father's black felt-tip pen from the cash register, and began to write.

He had finished, and stowed the letter beneath his sweater, when his father returned, asking, "Anything in?" with a sideways glance that slipped away when Jerry met it.

"Liniment is all."

"You might as well go home. It's going to be quiet."

It sounded like the old man was trying to be nice. Jerry saw through him. His father just wanted him out of there. "I'll stay," he answered.

"Whatever you want." His father retreated behind the prescription counter, fiddled with his small bottles.

Jerry knew what he was thinking. It was Jerry's fault. Everything that had happened. His father blamed him, his mother, too. But they had it turned around. *They* had done it. *They* had finally managed to separate Jerry and Jenny.

He'd refused to go to college. He wouldn't leave Jenny. How could he be expected to do that? He didn't know that when the time came they would have their way, and she would leave him. Laughing, smiling, she cried, "Goodbye, goodbye, I'll see you at Thanksgiving." He was there, at the college, at the end of the same week. She said, "Jerry, what are you doing here?" No laughter on her face. No welcome. But later, later, in the dark of the night, she reached for him whispering, "Oh, God, Jerry, how I've missed you." And the fire in her burned them both. Now it blazed only in him.

His father asked, "Are you coming?"

Jerry pushed himself upright. The lights were dimmed. The cash register emptied. His father had the money bag under his arm. He locked the door, tried it, and started for home. Jerry followed him.

Once in the house, they separated. Jerry went to his room. He sat beneath the lamp and stared at the dark square of the window. The transistor murmured from the floor beside him. He didn't remember that he'd first written to Quinn Monroe after hearing a bland voice say, "The United States Postal Service reminds all its patrons that zip codes speed the mail. If you want a letter delivered quickly, add zip codes to every address. This has been a public service announcement."

Jerry knew only that he had written twice. And it wasn't enough. He wanted more. He decided to drive the fourteen miles to Kansas City. He'd mail a third letter from there, too.

"If you're not happy where you are," the transistor voice whispered, "then pick up and go. Travel. Live a new life. Fly Pan Am to adventure. Seek and you will find. Just ask Pan Am."

Jerry wasn't a thinker or a planner. He simply waited, knowing what he wanted, and an idea blossomed in his mind full blown and prepared. He had always been that way. It was the same now.

He would go to Kansas City. And—he got up so suddenly that the chair tipped away behind him. And—Quinn Monroe . . .

Downstairs, in the kitchen, Elvira Lakas looked a question with her faded eyes.

"He dropped something," Mortimer said.

"No, Mort. I mean the other."

"Seems all right."

"You see? I told you. I knew you were wrong."

"Years wrong?"

"You said it seems all right."

"It does. Today. But what about yesterday? And the day before?"

"You probably made some small mistake."

"You think I don't know when stock goes off the shelf and the register doesn't show it? You think I've run my own business for thirty years without knowing what I should make in a month?"

"The town's shrinking."

"I know it as well as you."

"You're just against him, Mort."

"He's taking it, Elvira. He's being doing it for a long time. I just never wanted to admit it to myself or to you before."

"I don't believe you," she said quietly.

"There's so little coming in it shows. We can't go on."

"I don't believe you, Mort," she repeated, and left the kitchen.

But he knew she did. That's why she was retreating.

In a little while he heard the squeak of a drawer. The rustle of paper. He heard her murmur, "Now where could they have gone?" She was looking for Jenny's old pictures again.

CHAPTER 6

An airplane, flying low to duck beneath the ice storm over Riverton, rattled the windows of the homes in the crowded trailer park.

The sound brought Mary Baker awake with a heart-stopping jerk. Was it too late? Had she really managed to spoil it by oversleeping? She'd first suggested it two weeks ago. And had to back out. Since then she'd planned, considering every move. If she'd missed her chance she'd have to wait another week. She supposed she could, if necessary. But she didn't want to.

She turned her head cautiously on the pillow. Gus's deep ragged snore was a warning growl in the stillness. It was reassurance, too. The snarl, begun with a groan and ended with a snort, meant that he slept.

Her lips turned in a smile of delight. There was still time. She glanced fleetingly at the illuminated dial of the alarm clock on the built-in dresser. Five in the morning. Monday. She slid from the bed with care. She moved on chill bare tiptoes to the chair where Gus had tossed his brown corduroys the night before. At her touch his belt buckle made a fearsomely noisy sound. She froze, quick little pricks exploding on her suddenly cold skin.

Gus wheezed. He snorted and groaned. Through slitted eyes he watched as Mary slipped her hand into his trouser pocket. He could see the rounded curves of her small body through the lacy fabric of her baby-doll gown. He waited until she had his wallet open, her fingers within. Then he asked, "What in the hell are you doing there?"

She gasped, jumped. She dropped pants and wallet. "Oh, Gus, you scared me half to death. I thought you were sleeping."

"I know you did. But what do you think you're doing?"

"I wasn't doing anything." She edged away from the pants and wallet, both hands up to smooth her short dark hair, raising her breasts so that her pink nipples peeped over the ruffled neckline.

"Not doing anything," he mocked her. "That's just what it looked like." He had a deep, gravelly voice, roughened by too many cigarettes, and slightly overloud because of a small hearing loss developed in many years of working around the noise of heavy machinery.

In spite of how he sounded, he was grinning. "You were going to steal a bill out of there, weren't you?"

"Steal?" she cried. "I was not! Don't you dare say that!"

"Then what do you call it, sneaking into my money in the middle of the night."

"I was—well, I was going to borrow a little." She didn't expect to convince him. But she had to say something. A beat of silence. Then: "And not very much either."

"Borrow? So that's what you call it. And when were you going to pay me back? Also, with what?"

"Oh, Gus," she said hopelessly. "I don't know."

"Think about it," he insisted. And: "What do you want it for, anyhow?"

She stood in the shadowed corner, shaking her head back and forth, the chill running up her bare legs like a rising wind.

"And why couldn't you ask me? I give you whatever you want, don't I? All you've got to do is ask." He paused, went on suspiciously, "Or does it have to do with your Shirley? Did she put you up to it?"

Mary didn't answer. She continued to shake her head. She had been stupid. She had let herself be tricked by Gus one more time. Now he'd keep at her until she explained, and after she did, he'd keep at her until she promised. And she already knew that even if she did promise, it wouldn't mean anything. She wouldn't stick with it. Not when it had to do with Shirley. Gus knew it, too. But that wouldn't stop him.

His sudden laugh surprised her. "Aw, to hell with it. Come on back to bed." He threw the blankets off and patted the mattress.

There wasn't much room. He had a big body. It took more than half of the three-quarter bed, which was all the mobile home would hold. As she lay down beside him, she wished that they could have a house, like Shirley's, with room for a king-size, and a real kitchen instead of a galley. But Gus was used to trailers. He'd spent most of his life in them, moving from one construction job to another. She reminded herself that she was lucky he had wanted to settle down. They'd been in Riverton for five years now. He had a regular job with the highway department, keeping the big equipment on the roads. In the first three years they'd been married, they'd moved four times. She'd hated being thrust nose to nose with people who always remained strangers, pulled down unfamiliar streets in towns she never knew anything about.

Being settled was different, better. She was lucky in a lot of ways, and in spite of what Shirley always said, she knew it. Gus was a good man, and good to her, and she couldn't imagine what her life would have been if he hadn't come along. He was her whole family. Her father and mother and brothers and sisters. Her husband.

She snuggled against him, supposing that he had fallen back asleep. The alarm wouldn't go off for another three quarters of an hour.

The instant her thigh touched his hip, he chuckled, and his big hands slid under her gown to her breasts. "Fooled you again, didn't I?"

"I thought you were sleeping."

"Wanted to, expected to, but you gave me ideas. Seeing you, leaning over the chair."

"I'm sorry," she said automatically.

"Don't be." His voice was raspy. He pulled her closer. "I'm wide awake now." His arms enfolded her. "You're my little girl, Mary. Don't you forget it."

"Aw, Gus." She buried her face in his shoulder. "Aw, Gus. That's so good." The arms holding her. The broad hard chest with its coppery fur. She belonged to him, was part of him. All she'd ever had in her life was Gus. She didn't think of Shirley then.

His heat began to burn in her. She pulled off the baby-doll gown and threw it away into the dark, and leaned over him, so that her breasts curved around his night-stubbled cheeks, and she felt the nibble of his teeth at her enlarging nipples. My baby. She was thinking the words. Suck hard, my baby. But she was careful not to say them aloud. She used to. But she'd found out from a doctor in Brawley that there was something wrong with her inside plumbing, so now she didn't anymore. Just as Gus had given up saying, "Keep a woman barefoot and pregnant and in the kitchen, and she'll never give you any trouble." And: "All a woman needs is a baby in the pot, and two hanging on her hem. That'll stop her from getting big ideas." Suck hard, my baby, she thought again.

His big calloused hand went down her back, slowly, then down again, but further, and she shivered and pressed tighter, and he rubbed his face into her breasts.

"That hurts," she whispered.

"But it's nice and you like it." He rolled, his weight on her so that she felt the small hard bulge of his beer belly against her middle. He raised his head, grinned. "See what happens to you when you wake me up stealing money from my pants?"

"But I wasn't stealing," she said hotly. The good feeling was gone. Where there had been heat now there was cold. What was she going to do about Shirley? She'd apologized once, then again. Finally, unable to bear it, she'd looked into Shirley's wise eyes and said, "It's all set. The Greentree for lunch tomorrow." She couldn't back out now without telling Shirley what had happened. And she couldn't do that, either. It would spoil the whole day. And Shirley would say it all again. Mary didn't want to hear it. Mary didn't want to talk about it, to defend herself, to defend Gus. Shirley just didn't understand, and never would.

Gus put his mouth on Mary's lips. His tongue probed them open and went in. The heat came flooding back. She forgot about Shirley.

He was thick, hard, ropy against her. She touched him wonderingly, her fingers curled as if stroking velvet. He brushed her hand from him. "I want it to be good, to last. So don't move. Just let me." But when he thrust, her body rose up to meet his, and her round hips rolled, and while he was still saying, "Wait, wait," it was over. He collapsed on her, his heavy flesh enclosing her just as she enclosed him. They lay still, she hardly able to breathe. Then he moved away, sinking into sleep.

She was awake. She heard another plane fly low. The faint click of the propane tank. A dog barking far away. Ice crackled in the bare trees beyond the window. Half an hour later the alarm went off. She rose quickly, ducked into the minute bathroom.

By the time he rose, she had showered, made up her face, and dressed. She would change again, for meeting Shirley, but that would be after he left for the yards. She wasn't looking forward to the day anymore. She awaited it grimly, knowing that she'd have to explain that she didn't have the money for the Greentree Club lunch.

The coffee perked. The orange juice was squeezed. Three eggs sizzled in bacon fat. Four slices of bread, buttered with margarine, were stacked on a plate. The lunch sandwiches were ready: two hamburgers left over from the night before, lettuce and tomatoes and mayo. A slice of ginger cake that would choke a horse. He was a big man, and it took a lot to fill him.

He came in, nuzzled the back of her neck under her curls. "All ready for me?" And when she nodded, "That's my girl. I'm hungry enough to eat bear."

"I don't have bear," she told him, filling his coffee mug.

He drank half in a swallow. When he put the mug down he grinned at her. "You need some ready cash, don't you?"

"Yes, I do, Gus."

"All you got to do is ask. That's what I work for. To give you what you want." He dropped a twenty-dollar bill on the table. "That enough?" At her nod, he went on, "See how easy it is?"

She thanked him, smiling. But it flickered through her mind that it was as if he was paying her off. For making love with him. For getting him breakfast and fixing his lunch. She squelched the faint whisper. It was a Shirley thought. Gus was good to her. Nobody had ever been as good to her as he was. And wait until she told Shirley that their date was definitely on.

"Now, look," he said. "I mean it. Spend it for whatever you want. Okay? But not on Shirley Bacon."

Mary put a hand on the bill. Her eyes rounded and burned. Her lower lip drooped in a pout. "But you gave it to me," she wailed.

"The face on you—you look twelve years old going on five." He grinned. "I should've known she'd be behind it some way. Only I gave the money to you, for you. So don't throw it away on her."

"That's dumb," Mary cried. "If I want to, I will."

He ignored Mary's defiance. He shoveled eggs and toast into his mouth, and swallowed. Then: "It's the damnedest thing. We never fight about anything else. You're the easiest thing to get along with. But that Shirley—"

Mary covered her ears. "I'm not going to listen, Gus." It was an old argument, and she'd heard him say it too many times. "She's my *friend.*"

"That broad?" A jeer. "She wouldn't know how to be anybody's friend."

"That's what you think!"

"You're damn right it's what I think. It's also what I know. You suppose I haven't run into her kind before? You can find them in every diner in every town in every state. Wherever there's a highway, she'll be waiting. All I have to do is look at her and I can see it. She runs loose. And I don't like it."

"You found me in a diner," Mary retorted. "Are you talking about me, too?"

"Dumb bunny! You were different, and are different, and always will be. I knew the first minute I saw you." Now he grinned. "Also the first time I touched you. Hell, I damn near had to break your knees to get them open, didn't I?"

Her face stung. Her eyes ached. She shook her head vehemently.

"And I liked it," he went on, still grinning.

Liked it wasn't the word. That she had been a virgin surprised him, pleased him, and made him hers. He wasn't a man for second-hand goods. By the time they'd met, he'd been knocking around for twelve years. He'd seen every kind of woman there was. He knew only one good use for any of them. It was for that a man put up with them, because he couldn't get it anyplace but between a woman's legs.

But Mary was different. Sixteen then, and seeming even younger. Big-eyed still at coming out of the Harrisonburg orphanage, blushing at the talk she heard, scurrying off to the kitchen to hide when it got too rough for her. And that, for any of the other girls, was only the beginning. Not for Mary. She stayed herself. She kept on blushing when the talk got too rough. But Shirley was the whole bunch of them rolled into one. He looked at Mary, chucked her under the chin. "Come on, tell me. What do you see in that broad?"

"I told you. She's my friend."

He got up. "You can do better."

"I'm not going to listen to you, Gus."

"I'm your friend," he said.

"Sure. But that's different."

"Okay. Have it your way. But I'm telling you, you'll be sorry one of these days. Just don't come crying to me about it. I know what she is, even if you don't." He pulled on a heavy blue sweater, a fleece-lined jacket. He took the lunch box off the table. After he kissed her, he said, "Remember, I'm going out with the boys tonight. So don't get itchy if I'm a little late."

"Don't be *too* late. It gets lonesome."

"Watch TV or something."

He went out, not noticing that she hadn't answered.

When Mary saw him turn the pickup into the highway, she went to straighten up the bedroom. It took only a little while. That done, she threw together the ingredients for a beef stew, and set it on the burner. It would be more than half cooked by the time she left to meet Shirley. She'd finish it when she returned, with time to spare. If Gus didn't get home too late, or too full of beer, he'd want a hot meal.

By ten thirty Mary had finished the housekeeping chores. The trailer was dusted and swept and vacuumed, the bed made, the breakfast dishes washed and pans scrubbed. She was dressed and ready to go. It would take her just about half an hour to walk to the house on Engleton Road where Shirley lived.

She pulled on knee-high plastic boots made to look like leather, a heavy vest, and over it a black fake beaver coat. She tied a red scarf around her head, and then, sighing, took it off, and pushed it into her pocket.

As she went outdoors, a dog barked somewhere close by. She peered to right and left. It was only because she was afraid of them that they always barked at her. Gus never had that trouble.

When she saw that there were no dogs running loose between her and the highway, she set out. Each time a car passed her, she stepped way off on to the shoulder and waited, her eyes cast down, with fear a white-hot lava erupting in her throat. If those men could chase her once, it could happen again. Even in broad daylight. It was only when the passing car had gone on that she could move.

Always, as far back as she could remember, she'd been a little afraid of strangers. Not just men in cars. But anyone she didn't know. She thought it was because there had never been anything but strangers in her life. She didn't know how to tell Gus, had never even tried. But talking about it wouldn't have helped anyway. That was what her life had been. The orphanage, where she had been called Mary E., because four girls before her had been named Mary. When she was six she decided she wanted a last name, a family name, even if she had no family, and began to call herself Mary Easter. Nobody had bothered to question her. Nobody cared what she called herself. When she left the orphanage at sixteen, she got a job as Mary Easter, and not long after, she married Gus as Mary Easter, too.

At first, when she and Gus moved to Riverton, she was content, even though she didn't know anyone. She supposed they'd be moving on, so it didn't matter. But Gus had had enough of traveling, and when the state job came through he grabbed it. He put a white picket fence around the trailer lot, and built planters, and set up a plastic roof, so they had a front porch they could use during the short summers. Behind the trailer, he'd hung wash lines where she could dry the laundry.

She began to feel restless when she realized they were settled in for good. The walls started to close in on her. But there was nobody to talk to outside. The trailer park was filled with elderly retired couples. In summer the men fished. In winter they played poker. In summer the women sat with swollen feet propped on boxes, and told each other horror stories about trailer parks in Florida. In winter they huddled indoors, bundled in sweaters. The few younger women who lived close by were gone all day, working in the shoe factory or as domestics in Parkside Heights.

It got so bad for Mary, both inside and out, that she heard herself holding long conversations with herself, and no one to listen, no one to answer. One day she walked to the Turnpike Diner. She stayed as long as she dared, drinking cup after cup of coffee. Nearly drowning in it, just so she could hear a human voice. The atmosphere was familiar. The smells, the sounds, the movements. She knew the abbreviations. She felt as if she'd returned to the Harrisonburg diner where she'd met Gus.

She got to know Shirley in the Turnpike Diner. At first they talked about the weather, then about where they'd been and where they'd like to go. All that was covered while Shirley deftly plunked doughnuts on plates, and filled coffee cups, and spun hamburgers with fries from the pass-through window to the counter. She was quick on her feet, and quick with her tongue, too.

Mary began to quote Shirley at home. "Shirley," she'd say, "told me that if we'd moved to the north side, we'd have had a better deal on our rent."

"Shirley told you, eh?" Gus laughed. "Suppose you tell your Shirley that I checked good, and I found the best I could get. And since I'm paying for it, and I'm satisfied, what's it to her anyhow?"

Another night Mary said, "Shirley doesn't really want to be married. Not anymore."

"That's good," Gus retorted, "since I gather that she isn't, and if she talks that way, then she hasn't got any prospects either."

"But you're wrong. She's got the prospects. She doesn't want them. She's had three husbands. She says she's a bad picker, and with all her trying the most she got was headaches."

Gus frowned. "Where'd you meet this Shirley?"

"Oh, around." Mary was deliberately vague. Maybe Gus wouldn't like her to go to the Turnpike Diner every day.

"Around where?"

Mary shrugged. She mentioned Shirley less frequently after that. But the time came when she couldn't help herself. She had to bring the two halves of her life together. She hated the feeling of being divided. She wanted Shirley to meet Gus, and Gus to meet Shirley, never suspecting what might happen.

It was, from start to finish, a disaster.

Shirley had dressed up, bought a bottle of wine, and driven herself to the trailer park in her own car. Gus looked at her, looked at the wine, peered at the car beyond the fence. He retreated to his chair in front of the television set, and remained there, drinking beer until Mary put the roast beef on the table. Then he ate, grunted when spoken to, but contributed nothing to the evening, except when Shirley said, "There's going to be an opening at the diner. Want to come in half time, Mary?"

"Mary doesn't want to," Gus had said loudly.

Shirley's black eyes had narrowed. Her red lips curled at the corner. "Really? How come you don't let her talk for herself? She can say yes or no the same as you."

Gus had retorted, "Because I can talk for her. And she's glad to let me."

"Funny. I just happened to notice that here, tonight, she's as quiet as a little gray mouse." Shirley blew smoke in his face, and added, "At the diner she's always chattering away and laughing, too."

Mary's face had burned. She'd gotten up to bring dessert on wobbly knees. It was as if a bomb had been set, and a clock was ticking away seconds. And something terrible was going to happen.

Nothing did, except that when they were alone Gus said, "The trouble with her is she's got no kids to hold her down," and Mary winced. He saw, quickly pulled her to him. "You're different, Mary."

But after that night, he put his foot down. No. He didn't want Shirley coming back. It was his home, too, and that was how he felt. No, he didn't think she was smart, nor pretty, nor anything but a big-mouthed broad who didn't know her place. No. He didn't want to hear any more about her, either.

Mary continued her visits to Shirley at the diner, and found herself saying her friend's name to Gus just because she needed the pleasure of saying it. He didn't like that either. But it was the one thing Mary refused to give way on. She wouldn't let him talk against her friend, and, the other way around, she wouldn't let Shirley talk against Gus.

That began after the disastrous dinner. The next morning, Shirley put coffee before Mary, wandered off to take an order from a truck driver down the counter, and wandered back to say softly, "He give you a hard time after I left?"

Mary pretended not to understand. "What? Gave who?"

Shirley grinned. "You can't kid me. I know he spent hours talking me down. Now didn't he?"

"He's a good man."

"I'll bet. But you sure could do better. Everybody to their own, I guess."

Though Mary regularly protested, her friend's objections to Gus were listed, embellished, and embroidered upon. Gus wasn't sensitive. He wasn't fun. He wouldn't let Mary grow up. He was a meathead. He was just like any other man, in fact, and that was bad. He didn't amount to anything and never would. He treated Mary like dirt, and would treat any other woman he had the same way.

Mary believed none of what Shirley said, and believed none of what Gus said. She needed both of them in her life.

Now, as she walked up the front path to the house, Shirley opened the door. "Hi, I'll be right with you. I'm glad you're on time."

Surprised, Mary waited until she came out, buttoning her coat. "But we don't need to hurry, Shirley."

Shirley grinned. "Hop into the car with me. I made an appointment and I don't want to be late."

As she swung into Engleton Road, Mary asked, "An appointment where?"

"You'll see."

"I could have come earlier if I'd known."

"And you could have let me pick you up, too."

Mary shook her head. Shirley did enough for her as it was. That was one reason why Mary had been so determined about the lunch. It was a way of doing something back for her. Besides, if Gus had forgotten something, decided to come home . . .

"But we're going to make it in plenty of time," Shirley said. And added: "Nothing can stop us now."

CHAPTER 7

The Blue Bell Motel.

Mary sighed with relief. It had been a teeth-jolting ride.

Shirley parked. "Now, listen, Mary, and listen good."

Mary regarded her uneasily. Something was coming that would spoil the day she had planned for so long.

"You see how right I am, the things I tell you. And you'll see it this time, too." She fished a cigarette from her purse, lit it, and blew smoke at the windshield. "Once you let yourself think, that is."

"Shirley—"

"Wait. See, I noticed an ad in the paper a while back. There's a sales rep in town today. She's hiring girls for Becker's. You'd be perfect selling beauty products. She's expecting you because I called and made an appointment in your name. So let's go in."

"I can't. Gus wouldn't like it. You know what he said."

"Damn Gus," Shirley exploded. "Why should you be stuck all day in that trailer by yourself? Why shouldn't you do something, meet people, see things? Who passed a law saying you can't sell to the other women in that trailer park? Why, you'd make plenty right there. And he wouldn't even have to know if you didn't want him to."

"But I'd have to tell him. I'd want to," Mary said in a small voice.

"Grow up. Try it and find out what it's like."

"But I don't think I could sell anything," Mary protested. "I never have. So even if Gus said okay—"

"You ask him, he'll say no." Shirley thrust the car door open, stepped out. "Come on, will you? It's time to go in."

Because Shirley didn't wait, but went ahead, Mary followed her down a long dim-lit corridor, and paused before an open door.

A neat, hand-printed sign said BECKER'S. With a wink at Mary, a tug at her elbow, Shirley went in.

The room was large, bright. There were boxes on the bed, and books of paper, and sample cases of brightly colored bottles and tubes. The air was heady with scents. A tall, very slim young woman was speaking to a large girl dressed in wrinkled jeans.

The woman's hair was red-gold, heavy and shining in coils at the nape of her neck. She wore a white silk shirt under a red vest, and a flared dark blue skirt, and high red boots. She was like a picture in a magazine, Mary thought, shrinking inside. *She* could never be like that. *She* could never hold a job like that. She wished she were anyplace but in that room.

Quinn looked past the slumped shoulders of Lottie Furman and smiled. "Be with you in a minute." These two, she considered, looked more interesting. There was no hope for poor Lottie. Her nails weren't clean, nor her neck. She didn't care what she looked like, and never would, and Quinn knew she couldn't change her.

Within weeks of beginning to establish her crews, Quinn had learned that she could take any woman, except the Lotties of this world, and make her into a successful seller for Becker's. It was necessary only to convince her of what Becker's beauty aids could do for her. That conviction did it all. Very quickly Quinn had learned the tricks to accomplish that end.

Now she said to Lottie, "Just write your name and address on this card, and I'll let you know."

The girl flung down her pencil with a grunt.

Immediately Shirley gave her name, then Mary's, and went on, "I've got a job, so I can't take another on. But Mary here can do it, and she wants to."

"Have you ever sold before, Mary?" Quinn gave her full attention to the small dark-haired woman. Shirley was a natural. She could sell anything, any way. She'd need little training. But she'd have to be watched. She couldn't be trusted too far. Quinn was glad that Mary Baker was here for the interview.

Mary was shaking her head, unable to speak, though her eyes shone and a hopeful smile trembled at her lips.

"It doesn't matter if you haven't," Quinn told her easily. "I can train you in no time. And we have a few very simple rules that we follow. But first, have you ever used Becker's products?"

"No. But I've heard about them," Mary said. "And if they're what you use . . ."

Quinn grinned. "That's one of the advantages of the job. Anything you buy for yourself is on a twenty percent discount. And there are special bonuses and prizes for sales, too. Let me show you what we carry, and demonstrate at the same time. It's easy to learn the products that way." It was also easy that way to establish the self-confidence Quinn wanted to instill.

When Quinn waved her to a chair, Mary asked, "But do you really think I could do it?" By now she'd forgotten Gus.

"You've got nothing to worry about," Quinn laughed. "Just wait until we're through."

It always startled her to realize how much the façade counted. She herself, at that moment, did not feel like the district manager of a growing business. But no one would know it. The drive that morning from Passamody had been long and slow and tiring. The night's ice storm had silvered the trees and fences along the way, and glazed the All-State. She'd been hemmed with motor running for forty-five minutes on the outskirts of Riverton, where a tractor trailer had jackknifed. The sitting had worn her out. The thinking even more. Her winnings, less the 1 percent commission to the lottery agent, was in the bank. She'd paid for the new mink coat, the Gucci boots. Information was pouring in from a variety of travel sources, making the trip she planned more real than ever. But her excitement was constantly threatened. First there was Michael. Then there were the letters from Kansas City.

She shrugged her thoughts away to concentrate on Mary's uptilted face. It was fun to work on her. Her skin was smooth, unlined. Emollients, cleansers, fresheners, foundation . . . blush-on, rouge, powder. Eye liner and shadow, mascara. Lipstick and lip brush. While her hands deftly applied the various stuffs, she described Becker's policies. Women contact only their friends and neighbors, so they don't go door to door, dealing with strangers. There was a firm rule against leaving an order without receiving full payment, which prevented hard feelings and the need to return to collect. When she was finished, she displayed the packaged bubble baths and body oils and perfumed soaps.

Then, finally, some forty minutes after she had started, Quinn led Mary to the mirror, and stood back smiling.

Mary stared at herself, said, "Oh, how nice I look!" And when she left, she had two sample cases under her arm, an envelope of order books, and a perfect makeup job. She was lovely, her eyes aglow with delight and self-confidence under darkened black lashes, her cheeks rosy, her mouth sweetly pink.

Her excitement carried her through the elaborate lunch at the Greentree. Plans spun through her head. Every morning when she had finished the housework and laundry and stopped by for her coffee with Shirley, she would return to the trailer park. She would visit

each of the women, perhaps invite them for ginger cake and coffee, and demonstrate the products to them then. She imagined joyful giggling while she showed them the befores and afters, just as Quinn Monroe had done with her.

Shirley said, "If you could see yourself now."

Mary grinned. "Oh, I know I can do it." She paused for a deep breath, remembering Gus now. "I'll just have to persuade Gus. When he sees how much I want to, he'll understand."

"The thing is, I'm just baffled. Why'd you marry him, Mary? You could have any man you want."

Mary took the twenty-dollar bill Gus had given her, placed it neatly on the check at her right hand. Then, looking up at Shirley, she said, "I don't want to talk about Gus anymore."

Shirley met the cool level stare, grinned. "Hey, come on. I'm just teasing you." She got to her feet. "That was a beautiful lunch, and I thank you for it. Now let's go get me my lottery ticket. It's Monday, isn't it? I always buy my good-luck piece on Monday, as you know."

They drove the three blocks to the variety store. Mary had been there before. She'd tried the lottery twice and hadn't won, not even five dollars on the instant play, so she'd lost interest in it. But Shirley said, "Today's your lucky day, so you have to take a chance."

Still riding a wave of elation, Mary bought a fifty-cent ticket in the fifty-thousand-dollar superdraw, which she chose mostly because it was printed in her favorite colors, blue and green.

By the time she reached the trailer, the glow of delight had faded from her eyes. The money that Gus had given her was all gone. Worse, she'd have to tell him about Becker's, and that wouldn't be easy, she admitted to herself, now that the time was approaching.

It was even more difficult than she had imagined it would be.

Gus came home at eleven o'clock. He was beer-flushed and tired. He stared at her while he got out of his wraps. He kept staring at her while she put the coffee on the stove. Finally he said, "What's that goo you've got on your face?"

"Some new makeup I'm trying." She had powdered over and patched with the samples she had. She didn't pretend to herself that she looked as nice as she had after Quinn Monroe worked on her, but she considered that she was still more than passable.

He didn't think so. "It looks funny on you."

"I'll wash it off," she told him, heart sinking.

He saw the sample cases and his frown disappeared. "Did you buy yourself some pretties?"

"Not exactly."

"Then what?"

But she served him rhubarb pie before she began to tell him about Quinn Monroe and Becker's and how simple it would be to sell the cosmetics, and how much fun, too.

His frown returned. He said, "No, forget it. Get that stuff back to the Monroe woman in the morning."

"But it's just around the trailer park."

"No, Mary." And then, jowls reddening: "It's Shirley. She put you up to it."

"I want to do something," Mary cried. "You can't always blame Shirley."

"I want you here, home. Where you belong. Not running around. Not selling that goop, as if you could anyway."

"I could. I know it, Gus. As soon as I saw how I looked in the mirror, I realized I could. If only you let me try."

"And end up owing the company God knows what? Not on your life. Who do you think you are anyhow? What've you ever done? You're not Shirley, no matter how much you think you want to be. Hell, she could package shit and call it cinnamon and sell it. But that's not you. So get smart."

Mary gave in, knowing he was right. She'd never make a go of a business. Why bother to try?

They were in bed, side by side, but not touching; quiet and unmoving, but both awake.

Gus said into the dark, "The thing is with you, you're so softhearted. I can just see it. Some old bag gives you a forty-dollar order, and when you deliver, she's all promises for the next day, so you leave the junk. The next day comes. You're there, bright-eyed and bushy-tailed. She's out. From then on she'd always be out."

"Never mind," Mary answered. "It's okay."

"It's not okay." But it was moments before he went on: "The other thing is, that's why you were stealing the twenty dollars. It had to do with Shirley."

"I wasn't stealing," Mary cried. And: "She always does things for me. So I wanted to take her out for lunch to someplace special."

"What things does she do for you?" Gus demanded.

Mary rolled over, buried her head in the pillow. "Just things," she whispered, and squeezed her eyes shut and bit her lip to keep from crying.

In the morning, Gus drove her to the Blue Bell Motel. He waited while Mary went in.

Quinn listened to her apologies, and accepted the return of the samples and order forms. She saw that Mary was upset, close to weeping, but said only, "I'm sorry, but don't worry. I understand. And if you change your mind sometime, just leave a message for me here. I come by every other Monday, and I'll be glad to have you sign on."

They walked out to the lot together. Mary watched until Quinn drove off on her way to St. Mary's City, then climbed into the pickup. She said nothing to Gus.

"Did she give you any trouble?" he asked.

"No."

"You going home?"

Mary hesitated. Then: "I'm going to stop for coffee first."

"To cry on Shirley's shoulder?"

"So I can tell her," Mary answered.

That, too, proved harder than she had expected it to.

Shirley's black eyes flashed. "Well, don't think I'm surprised! I know your Gus. And I know you, too. But I thought maybe you'd have the stomach and spine to make it this time." She leaned over the counter, patted Mary's hand. "What's the difference?"

Mary didn't try to prolong the coffee hour that day. As soon as she had finished, she left. She walked back to the trailer park, her shoulders hunched against the cold. Her numbed fingers fumbled for her key ring. A small bit of blue and green cardboard fell at her feet. She bent to pick it up. The lottery ticket. She could hear Shirley saying, "Today's your lucky day!"

But it hadn't been. It wouldn't be. She jammed the ticket into her pocket, and opened the door and slammed it behind her as hard as she could.

Gus, thinking all day on the job about the sag to Mary's shoulders as she trudged away from him, blamed Shirley. She made Mary restless, leading her into wanting to be what she wasn't. Shirley was interfering in Gus's marriage, and his life. He didn't like it.

When he left the yards he continued to brood on it. After a few tall beers at the Rocking Horse Café he decided to tell her so. He had another few beers to give her time to get off work and get home. When he judged it was about right, he drove to her house on Engleton Road. Mary had pointed it out to him one day.

He parked the truck and sat staring at the dark shadows. Mary was expecting him soon, but she could wait a little longer. This was something he had to do.

Judging by the unlit windows, Shirley still wasn't home. He'd wait. Now was the time to tell her off for good.

A car crunched in the snow, rolled to a stop behind the pickup. Its lights went out. Shirley.

He got out of the truck.

She leaned inside her car to gather some large grocery sacks. Her ass tipped up; a curved handful. She straightened, came toward him. She wore high-heel boots, slim and tall. Her plaid coat fit like a banana skin.

When she was close enough to recognize him, she stopped, stared. Then, with a grin tilting her mouth: "Hiyah, Gus."

"I want to talk to you," he said gruffly.

She shrugged, went up the path to the house. Her hips swung saucily at him. Her thighs rippled under the swing of her coat. At the door, she shoved the bundles into his arms. "Hold these while I open up."

Inside, she stripped off her coat, flung it over a banister. She switched on a lamp, then crossed her arms under her breasts so that they jutted out at him. "Well?"

He put the sacks on the floor. When he straightened his jowls were red and his eyes narrowed and hot. "You stay away from my wife. I don't want you talking her into getting jobs she doesn't need, nor talking against me neither. We were okay until you came along, and we're going to be okay again."

"Why don't you tell it to Mary?"

"I'm telling it to you." He came closer, glared down at her. "So you listen."

She grinned. Then, abruptly, she turned away, hips swinging again. She jerked the door open. "Get out of here, Gus Baker. I'm not interested in what you have to say."

He kicked the door shut. "I'll go when I'm ready." The bundles on the floor suddenly tipped, and a tangerine rolled free. He stepped on it as he went to her.

She stood her ground. "My, my, I suppose I ought to be scared. Well, Gus, you can play the ape all you want to. It won't bother me." He didn't plan it. It simply happened. One minute he was going to slap her smart-mouth face, the next minute he had pulled her into his arms.

The scent of tangerine was all around them as he walked down the hall, holding her lithe hot body to his, finding the back bedroom without knowing where it was, and falling onto the red satin quilt, tearing at her clothes while she tore at his.

The morning alarm went off. A faint gray filled the room. Mary turned on her side, yawned aloud. But Gus didn't move. She slipped from the bed, padded into the bathroom, and from there into the galley. She filled his lunch box quickly, and when she finally heard him stirring, she started the eggs for his breakfast.

She waited, but he didn't come to her. She waited some more. Then, when she couldn't stand it, she opened the bathroom door, and whispered, "Gus? Gus, I'm sorry. Really I am. Let's make up right now. Yesterday was so dumb and awful."

He had shaving lather like a mask on his face and his eyes were squinted and she couldn't read his expression. It seemed a long time before the familiar grin came, and he said gruffly, "There's nothing to make up, Mary. Just forget it, that's all."

She found the ticket when she looked in her purse to see how much money she had. She crumpled it in her small fist. Lucky day! In a pig's eye! That was when it had started. This funny thing that had happened between her and Gus.

They pretended that she'd never talked to him about Becker's. She'd said she was sorry, and he'd said to forget it, and they acted as if everything were the same. But she knew better. Some small thing was different. Maybe because Gus stayed out for his beers more often and later. Maybe because he never quite looked her straight in the face. Lucky day!

She tossed the crumpled ticket on the table. It rolled off. As she bent to pick it up, she wondered what would have happened if she'd won.

She saw Gus's face when she put a check in his hand. Five thousand dollars! How he would grin! Not because of the money, but because she'd done something right. He'd forget he'd ever been mad at her.

With her coat on, she stepped into the cold March wind. She went to the Turnpike Diner. It was the first time that she could remember not telling Shirley what she planned to do.

They talked about the weather, and grocery prices, and a bank robbery the day before. Mary didn't mention Gus, and neither did Shirley. After two cups of coffee, Mary said she had to go shopping. Shirley didn't try to persuade her to stay longer.

At the variety store where she and Shirley had gone before, Mary bought a ticket for the weekly draw. She memorized its number on the way home.

That Thursday, as soon as Gus had gone to work, she hurried out for a newspaper. Her hands shook as she opened it to the state news page. Blue 01 Green 23 Yellow 09. Her heart sank. She dropped the newspaper and the lottery ticket into a trash bin. It was silly. She wasn't going to try it anymore.

But by Tuesday, against all good sense, she had begun to think that miracles *could* happen. And what did she have to lose except a dollar? She went back to the variety store, bought another ticket in the weekly draw. Again she memorized the number on the way home. Green 21 Blue 30 Red 18.

On Thursday she hurried out for the paper. She laughed at herself as she turned the pages. The number leaped at her from a large box. Green 21 Blue 30 Red 18.

She didn't believe it! Things like that didn't happen. Not to people like her. Not to a nobody like Mary Baker. But that's what the ticket said. Green 21 Blue 30 Red 18.

She was so happy that she cried. Then she laughed. She floated halfway to the Turnpike Diner to tell Shirley, but decided that Gus must hear it first. She hurried back to the trailer. She baked a chocolate cake, and made shepherd's pie, watching the clock.

Gus came home late, tired, beer-flushed.

She was at the door, waiting. She threw herself into his arms, crying, "Gus, Gus, you won't ever believe this, but I won! I won in the lottery!"

He said, "What? Have you gone nuts?"

"Three times," she said. "I only bought three tickets, a dollar apiece, and they're going to give me fifty thousand dollars!" She showed him the ticket, the number in the paper.

Finally he knew it was true. He grabbed her, picked her up, did a shuffle around the small room, swinging her in the air.

He broke out some whiskey and they got high together.

They talked about celebrating, and he spoke of all he could do with so much money. Like buy a new pickup for himself. A real fur coat for Mary. They laughed together, and tried to dance in the small space between the chairs, and every few minutes, he said, "I don't see how you did it, that's all. I just don't see how you pulled it off."

Finally she sat in his lap, and stroked his coppery hair and nuzzled him, and he patted her cheek, grinning. "Well, all I can say is, regardless of how you pulled it off, three for fifty thousand's a pretty good investment."

"A house is a good investment, too," she said. She didn't care about a real fur coat. Gus already had a pickup.

"We'll see," he told her, and hugged her.

But when she went to bed that night she lay staring into the darkness. The miracle had happened. And nothing was changed.

When she told Shirley the next day, there was a brief flurry of excitement. Shirley screamed, laughed, demanded, "What're you going to do with it?"

"Whatever Gus wants," Mary answered, and thought of the house.

Still laughing, Shirley cried, "I knew that's what you'd say."

News spread quickly through the trailer park. The children pointed at Mary, the neighbors stared. Some came to visit, to ask wistfully if she'd be moving to Florida now. Others told her their various troubles. One woman, Molly Farran, a maid on Parkside Heights, wished her good luck and asked her in for coffee. It didn't matter because Mary already knew that nothing had changed.

Soon after, she went to the variety store to have her ticket validated. A week passed. The check came in the mail. Twenty percent was deducted for federal taxes. One percent went to the variety store. Gus put $39,500 into the bank along with his pay. Then he and Mary stopped in at the next-door People's Fair to have a cup of coffee.

While she'd signed her name to the check, Mary had been excited. Now the good feeling was gone. She'd had her miracle, but everything was the same. She leaned an elbow on the counter, and sighed.

CHAPTER 8

The house was old, weathered gray. Its side windows overlooked the Rolls-Royce dealership. The front ones faced the Old North Road over a neglected yard.

It was neglected within, too. The rugs worn, the easy chairs sprung. That didn't matter to Jerry. It was a place to stay, to rest. It was in Elkhorn.

He was close now. He would see her again with his own eyes. He would see the girl who used to live with Jenny. The girl he'd watched walk between two policemen across a distant lobby. Whose name, he'd later heard from whispering tenants, was Quinn Monroe.

He stood on the threshold of the room, a half smile on his lips. He nodded slowly, while his new landlady, Mrs. Varnick, tried to make him feel at home.

"Plenty of towels in the cupboard next door to the bath. And an extra quilt, too, if you need it, which you might. Our March winds blow cold. The Burger Barn has breakfast. Specials, with ham and eggs. The heater in the corner works, but you'll be careful, won't you, Mr. Lakes?"

He'd already corrected her twice. This time he let it go. "I'll be careful," he said.

"And anything you need, you tell me. I want you to be comfortable, and have a good stay and pretty soon you'll be as good as new."

He had told her he was recuperating from an illness and had come to Elkhorn for the fresh air and peace and quiet. He longed for that quiet now.

He thanked her, went in, and closed the door on her disappointed face.

He'd spent some ten days in Passamody, getting the feel of the area, driving back and forth from Elkhorn, until he was sure it was better. Now he was sure. It was closer. Nobody would notice him.

He'd wanted to look like everybody else around so he'd let his hair grow a little longer. It had developed a wave and curls over his ears. He wore a new red-and-blue plaid parka and dark corduroy pants and work boots, an outfit he'd seen a hundred times around Passamody and Elkhorn. His dusty tan sedan had new plates and new tires, too.

He switched on the transistor, turned it low, and sat down with paper and a felt-tip pen. When he had finished writing, he rose and yawned, hardly listening while a voice from the radio whispered, "Sheriff Marion Dade, of Fielding County, reports an outbreak of vandalism against automobiles. Tires have been slashed, windshields broken, paint scratched. The sheriff blames juveniles, and promises full prosecution when the perpetrators are caught. In Cannon County, Sheriff Burns describes an outbreak of pet killings. Seven animals, dogs and cats, have lately been slaughtered. Guns in the hands of irresponsibles are behind this carnage, the sheriff says." And briskly: "The State Lottery Commission announces that ticket sales are ahead for this time last year, and tells us about Mary Baker, age twenty-four, of the Riverton Trailer Park, in Riverton, who this month won $50,000 in the weekly draw. Mary and her husband Gus, she says, will probably buy a real house right there in Riverton." A trill of music. Then: "And now the weather . . ."

Mary Baker, twenty-four, another winner. She was married and alive and had all that money. Did she know how lucky she was? Was she grateful for her happiness? The two of them, Mary Baker and Quinn Monroe, had everything. But being alive is good and bad. How would they know the good without the bad?

Jerry took his transistor with him when he went to the bed. It was wide and deep. He fell upon it, and let himself think of Jenny.

"You dreamed it," Mortimer Lakas said.

But Elvira opened the door and peered into bright sunshine. Then, sighing, she agreed. "I guess. But I swear I heard him drive in during the night. Just like he's always done before. Only the car's not there."

"You didn't hear him. And you won't."

"But he's always come back. After a week, maybe two, he's always turned up again."

Mortimer didn't answer.

"You think he's gone for good, don't you?" she asked. And added softly, "Like Jenny."

"Yes. And good riddance to bad rubbish."

He'd said the same thing when Jenny disappeared. Elvira couldn't bear it then. She couldn't bear it now. She screamed, "Don't say that, Mort!" and saw the desolation in his eyes.

CHAPTER 9

The cold wind swirled through the door when Quinn opened it, hurrying into the house ahead of her and fading with a quick rustle in the windowsill plants.

Helen leaned over the banister to call, "A good week?"

Quinn nodded, sat down to take off her high boots.

"Michael phoned. He's back from Boston. He said he'd stop by later." Helen came slowly down the steps, wiping her hands on her hips. Red paint smears stained her already grimy shirttails. "And the mail's there," she went on.

Quinn had already seen the stack on the coffee table. Letters from those charity organizations which had not yet given up on her, maybe a demand for help written in smeared pencil. And what else?

"Aren't you going to look at it?" Helen asked.

"Just junk," Quinn shrugged.

"I've noticed those envelopes with no return address."

"They're junk, too." She took up the mail. Some travel folders she'd written away for. Air India . . . a howdah swaying on an elephant's back . . . Norway's glistening glaciers . . . And beneath— She glanced up at Helen. "Bonanza. Now there are two."

"And they worry you." Helen went on after a pause. "If they're nasty, throw them away."

But Quinn didn't. She went to her room. The two envelopes were sticky with the sweat of her hands. She knew who had written them. The black felt-tip pen, the neat script, had become familiar to her. *A Friend.* A nameless faceless person in Kansas City, whose words wished her well, yet seemed to contain an unspoken threat.

The two postmarks seemed to leap up at her. *Cleveland. Indianapolis.*

She read both notes quickly. The first said, *Are you having fun? What have you bought with your winnings? How have they changed your LIFE? Aren't you happy to be ALIVE?* The second said, *I was just sitting here after a long dull day, thinking how lucky you are, so I decided to write you again to wish you joy of your good fortune in this LIFE.*

Cleveland. Indianapolis. She imagined a road map. Kansas City. Indianapolis. *A Friend* was coming east, coming closer.

From below, she heard voices. Helen's. Then Michael's deeper tones. There was a quick little leap of warmth within Quinn. She'd think of the letters later. She put them away with the others, and went downstairs.

His dark hair was wind-tousled, his blue eyes bright. He thrust a bunch of daffodils at her. "It won't be spring here for a while, even with the off-and-on thaws. But these are out in Boston."

She found a vase, put them in water, asked Michael how his trip had been.

"I got a good tape out of it. But I'll have to go down to the Washington area soon." He should have gone before but had put it off. The discipline that had always kept him at his work before was faltering now. He'd settle at the desk, find himself thinking about Quinn. He'd go for a walk to clear his head, and end up in the car, driving north to be with her.

She was smiling at him. "When you do go, give my reagrds to the Federal Triangle."

Later, at his house, they made love. She didn't mention the letters.

Saturday morning. Quinn heard the mail truck. She hurried outside. The letter she found in the box had been stamped Boston. Only a hundred and some miles from Elkhorn. Two hours by automobile. Maybe twenty-five minutes by plane.

The next afternoon, telling no one, she drove through Elkhorn, past Mrs. Varnick's house and the Rolls-Royce dealership to the State Police substation. She carried with her the letters she had received. A thin blond man was at the front desk. His name was Lacy Pickett.

When she explained briefly, asked to whom she should talk, he smiled, gestured to a chair close by. "You talk to me."

She seated herself, put the letters before him. "Ever since I won the lottery in February these have been coming."

She kept her dark eyes fixed on his face, trying to read his expression as he examined the envelopes, then studied the notes.

When he was done, he said ruefully, "Looks as if you've made yourself a friend."

"Is there anything that strikes you as peculiar?"

"Kook letters are always peculiar. These are mild compared to some." He leaned back in his swivel chair. "Big money attracts attention. Usually it's worse. Dirty, I mean."

"That's just it. Since they *are* nothing, why would anybody bother to write them?"

"You can't figure out how a kook's mind works." The state trooper grinned. "I noticed the postmarks, too. You're worried that he's coming closer, and wondering why. But these people never do anything."

"What would he get out of it then?" she asked.

"His kicks." The trooper put his hand on the letters. "Tear them up. If more come, ignore them. It'll stop soon. I've been watching since the lottery began. Something always happens on the big wins. Some folks want to just go about their business and they find they can't. Their lives are changed. Some start running, thinking they can chase their daydreams down the road. If this is all that happens to you, you'll be lucky again."

"It's been so long now," she said slowly. "Isn't there something I can do?"

"You know anybody in Kansas City?"

She shook her head.

"So there's nobody to start with. And no way to do a trace job. The paper and envelopes come from any dime store. There are a million black felt-tip pens. And I don't see a threat to make us want to get into it anyway."

"But they *are* coming closer."

"That doesn't mean much. Anybody can stick these into a larger envelope, and have them dropped into a box wherever." The trooper went on slowly. "It's the publicity. A price you pay for winning. But nothing will happen." He got to his feet. She was a pretty girl, and if he hadn't been married, with four small sons, he would have prolonged the conversation. As it was, he had paperwork up to here. "Go home and enjoy your good luck," he said. And, opening the door for her, "If anything more turns up, come and tell me about it."

She shuddered as she got into the Rabbit. He'd told her only what she had expected, feared he would. There was nothing to do but wait for the letters to stop coming.

That night, as Lacy Pickett ate his midnight supper, having just come in off duty, his Eva said, "You know, I think Mrs. Varnick's about the happiest old lady in town these days. My sister May told me that she's really satisfied with the roomer she took in. He's quiet as a mouse. Only plays his little radio at a whisper, which is like having company, she says."

"That's nice," Lacy said absently. And: "Any more coffee in the pot?"

The same night Quinn and Michael went for a ride in the countryside.

She had been quiet.

"A penny for them," Michael said.

"Not worth even that."

He slid a glance at her, looked back at the road. "You have a way of disappearing sometimes, Quinn."

"I'm right here," she said, smiling.

"Your mind isn't," he answered soberly.

"I was thinking about tomorrow, Passamody, and Riverton, and what I have to do."

"I'd rather you think about me. About us."

She said, "What we have is good, Michael. Can't we leave it at that?"

"No. I want more, Quinn. I'll have more." He reached out, caught her hand in his. "You already know that."

She looked at their linked fingers, then drew her hand from his. "That's just it," she said slowly, softly, "I can't promise you more. There's just now, this little time. Who knows what will happen? To you. To me. Who really knows? You're getting in too deep."

"Let me worry about myself, Quinn. I'm a big boy," he said roughly. "I'm not afraid. Why should you be?"

She was silent.

"And what about love?" he demanded. "Do you think you can ignore it, live without it? What makes you think you can get a contract, anyway? Who do you get it from? How? You just take your chances in life, and hope for the best."

"That's what I'm doing," she flared.

The thought of Katherine was in his mind. He said angrily, "You carry this independence bit too far. You're not one of those ball-breakers who uses a man and dumps him. So why pretend you are?"

She yelled, "If that's how you see me, then maybe that's just what I am. And since you can't change me, and you don't like it, maybe that's what we'd better deal with." It hurt to say it, but she had to. She remembered Lew Selby.

"Jesus," he said, "what're we fighting about?" He swerved the car to the side of the road, stopped. He pulled her into his arms. "Let's just let it go for a while. Okay?"

She nodded against his shoulder. "Okay."

But as he left Westbrook Road, he said, a faint smile on his mouth, "I hope I *can* change you, Quinn. Just a little for now. Helen told me—"

"Helen!" Quinn said sharply.

He went on, "—about some letters you've been getting."

"It was wrong of her," Quinn said.

"Why are they a secret?" he demanded.

"I prefer not to discuss them."

"Even with me?"

"Even with you."

"Don't you feel that I'm involved?"

"You aren't, Michael."

"But I am. I'm part of your life. Whatever concerns you concerns me. Whether you like it or not."

Helen had said Quinn was receiving something through the mail that frightened her. Helen didn't know what.

He was determined to know. He said, "I want to read those letters, Quinn."

"There's nothing to read. I took them to a trooper at the State Police substation. He said they'd stop coming after a while."

Michael didn't answer. He made the sharp turn into Old Barn Road, guided the car over ice ruts, and spun it through the opening in the stone wall. He jammed the brakes on, cut the lights. Only then, turning to her, he said angrily, "You were concerned enough to talk to Lacy Pickett. Yet you never told me what was happening."

"I had no reason to."

"Here we go again," he retorted. "But never mind for now. I'm going to see those letters."

She shrugged. With him at her heels, she went into the house. She went up to her bedroom and returned to him holding the bundle of envelopes.

He flipped the notes out and read them in sequence. He read them once more, slowly. When he had finished he raised thoughtful eyes to her tense watching face. "These seem to be from someone who wants to wish you well."

"I told you."

Face bland, voice expressionless, he tossed the letters aside. "Forget them. They'll quit coming, just as Lacy Pickett said." But Michael himself felt a certain uneasiness. There was an odd undertone to the good wishes. And there was the movement from Kansas City east. Still, he wanted to reassure her. He went on, "I'm certain every winner *does* get this kind of thing."

She didn't answer him.

He studied her. What he saw was more than an uneasiness that mirrored his own. It was a taut controlled fear, and as he kissed her good-night, he knew that she was unconvinced by what he'd said, that her body was stiff and her eyes shadowed with something like terror.

The next morning the sun was up and clear, but the air was bitter cold. She finished loading the Rabbit, then checked the mailbox. Another letter was there. This time it was mailed in Passamody, just eight miles from Elkhorn.

Her heart gave a little jump of fright. She jammed the envelope into her pocket. There was nothing to be done. While she warmed up the car, she told herself that neither Lacy Pickett nor Michael had seen a threat in the letters. Perhaps there was none there. Perhaps the threat *was* in her own mind. She drove cautiously down the lane, past the stand of birches at the big curve, and headed toward the Old North Road.

A sheaf of dry blowing hay reminded her of leafy-roofed native huts. Tahiti. She'd write for information. It was time, too, to set a target date. June. That would be a good month for starting out.

When she left Elkhorn there were two lumber trucks behind her. Following them was a dusty tan sedan.

CHAPTER 10

It was midweek in St. Mary's City.

Quinn searched her purse for a pen, saw the note she'd carried since the Monday before.

I hope you're enjoying your good fortune. May the spring sun shine on you, and the summer sun warm your days. And your money bring you your heart's desires. A Friend.

The words burned in her mind. She willed the feeling away with an effort that tired her.

The night before she had made notes of what she'd need to buy for her round-the-world trip. New luggage. An all-weather coat. Now she added two suits. Sighed. Put the list away.

From her window in the Capitol Hotel she could see the state house dome, and on the ridge above, the still-bare trees of Belair. She glanced at her watch. Ten thirty.

A knock at the door. She checked a card. Yes. It would be Ellen Logan, coming for an interview, and on time to the minute. A plus.

Quinn welcomed the girl in, immediately liking what she saw. An enthusiastic and hopeful smile. An attractive outfit. Quinn introduced herself. Then: "I'm glad you came by, Miss Logan."

"I've been anxious to talk to you," Ellen answered. "I'm sure I can do the job. I know I want to try."

An hour later, aglow with excitement, her face lightly made up to highlight its natural charm, she hurried down to the bus stop, clasping a sample case under her arm.

"Antaddy! Antaddy!" Ellen burst through the glass doors into the hush of the country club lounge, bringing with her the outdoor chill and that undefinable aura of anticipation that Adelaide Herman ruefully equated with youth. "Antaddy, am I late? I'm sorry if you've been waiting long."

Ellen's high sweet voice bridged the space between them, while Adelaide lifted a white gloved hand, smiling, and looked past the girl's shoulder to see if Evan had come with her. Adelaide dismissed the hope she had had as irrational. Evan needed time to get over being angry.

"What a rush it's been," Ellen cried, and beamed, as she bent to touch warm lips to Adelaide's cheek. "I'm so glad we could get together today, I just had to talk to you."

Ellen was nineteen, tall, slender, built for the thick layered look of the season. Her parka, the two sweaters beneath it, and her dark-blue trousers had come from L. L. Bean in Freeport, Maine, and were Christmas gifts from Adelaide.

The knot of worry eased in Adelaide's throat. It was always that way when she saw her goddaughter, the only child of her best friend at Radcliffe.

"You look wonderful," Ellen said. "But you always do."

"Thank you. I believe it's the mink. It somehow manages to conceal effectively the face above it."

"Oh, you! Playing yourself down again. It's bad psychology. People value you only as much as you value yourself."

"I'll try to remember. "

"I've so much to tell you, Antaddy."

Antaddy stood for Aunt Addy, and Ellen had begun to use it at the age of three. It carried with it the history of their knowing each other and loving each other. When Ellen's mother died, it was Adelaide that Ellen had phoned. When Ellen's father's business failed, and he was able to manage only the bare tuition for the state university, Adelaide had attempted to help. With the way things were, she wondered how long she could continue.

Now she said, "Let's go in and have lobster while you tell me what's been going on."

Falling into step beside Adelaide, Ellen said, "It's ridiculously expensive. Lobster, I mean. I've been noticing the prices."

"Lobster along with everything else," Adelaide answered, though she herself hadn't noticed and didn't intend to start now. And if George complained about the month's bill at the club, then let him. It was his fault Adelaide never had Ellen at the house anymore.

They were seated by the maître d', who knew Adelaide Herman well. She was a frequent guest, and her husband was on the board of directors. The maître led Adelaide and Ellen to a round table in a comfortable corner. Cut glass gleamed on white linen. A single red carnation gave off a spicy scent.

Ellen touched it. "Imagine. In late March, Antaddy."

Adelaide grinned. "They tried plastic roses, but the board wouldn't stand for it. Members who couldn't tell a dahlia from a dandelion were absolutely incensed."

"The board . . . oh, yes," Ellen murmured.

"Some standards must be maintained." Adelaide widened her twinkling blue eyes.

At the back of her mind, she was thinking of George. She was teasing Ellen now. But she hadn't been teasing anyone when she watched and heard George slurp his coffee that morning. In twenty-two years of marriage he had never noticed that he couldn't hear *her* drink her coffee. A small thing. But how it rankled after twenty-two years, and the anguish those years had brought with them.

The waiter appeared, bent to attention. Adelaide ordered lavishly. Lobsters. Salads. Fried potatoes. Coffee later. Leaning back, she smiled at Ellen. "And now, begin."

"It's what made me late." Ellen braced both elbows on the table, arching over them to narrow the distance between her and Adelaide. "I saw this ad on the school bulletin board. 'Young woman wanted to sell products of nationwide cosmetics company.' That's Becker's, of course. The young woman's me."

"Then you've applied for a job."

"Applied for and got," Ellen crowed. "And you should see the girl who hired me. Oh, she's something else! If I could ever look like her—"

"You do nicely as yourself. I wouldn't want you to look like anyone else."

"But you love me, Antaddy. That's different."

"You ought to have told me you were short on money, Ellen." If it weren't for the way George was, Ellen could have lived at the house. But Adelaide knew him too well. She'd seen him notice that Ellen was grown up now, lovely and young. She noted that what had been an unofficial uncle's casual embrace had become something more. Pats on the fanny. Quick shoulder pinches. That was why Adelaide kept George and Ellen apart. She didn't want her goddaughter to suffer the guilty embarrassment that would become a wedge between her and Adelaide.

"You already do too much for me," Ellen was saying. "And I'll have all I need with what I earn from Becker's."

"It'll cut into your college experience, Ellen."

"It's going to be part of it. I guess you don't know, but many of the girls work. I'd have done it before if I could have found a job. There's awful competition for every penny to be earned around here."

Adelaide recalled that there had been working students when she was in school. She hadn't known any well. Adelaide and her friends received allowances from home, banked them, wrote checks, rarely balancing their accounts. It was different now, just as the world was different now.

She raised her blue eyes. "I'm proud of you, Ellen." And: "I want to be your first customer. What do you recommend?" She refused to listen to Ellen's protests. "Put me down for a twenty-dollar order. You decide what I should have."

The waiter came with the hot platters. Ellen attacked the lobster with gusto, while Adelaide picked daintily at hers, and thought of Evan.

The hard knot in her throat swelled so that for a moment she lost her breath. No matter what George said, she would see to it that Evan finished college. It was what she had planned since his birth, and nothing would take that from her. A degree was his passport back into the world to which he was entitled, the life she wanted for him. By marrying George, she had made it more difficult. Why hadn't she known? Why hadn't she listened to her parents? What was it that George had offered her then that had seemed so necessary? She could no longer remember.

But she knew it had been wiped out in a single instant some six weeks before Evan was born. She had been in town for a visit to the doctor. She decided to stop and see George. Heavy, graceless, her once slim body distorted by her pregnancy, but joyful over it, she passed the secretary's empty desk, and quietly opened George's door, expecting to surprise him.

He never knew that she had seen him, his big bulky frame covering the girl beneath him. He never knew that Adelaide had heard the animal sounds they made, and smelled their sweat.

She had retreated silently, wept private tears, and learned hate instead of love.

Only pride kept her with George then and later. She couldn't face going home to hear her mother say, "I told you so." To hear her father mutter, "It's what you get for marrying out of your own kind." She concentrated all her love on Evan for that was all she had.

When Ellen and Adelaide had finished lunch, Adelaide led the way outside. It was still very cold. An icy wind drove across the parking lot. Ellen's hair floated around her face.

She smiled, "Thanks for everything, Antaddy."

"I want to make a stop. Then I'll drive you back to the campus."

Ellen agreed, settled in the car, and Adelaide drove to Howard Street, where she parked near a boutique. "I want to pick something up here. Come along."

It was steamy inside. Racks of silk scarves brightened one wall. St. Laurent. Schiaparelli. Vera. Adelaide took several down; a blue in a geometric design, a pale green with pink flowers, a yellow and purple. "Which one, Ellen?"

"Antaddy, no!"

"Your hair," Adelaide said. "I mean it, Ellen. I want you to have one, and I'll have one myself. Just choose, and don't argue."

When Adelaide paid for the two scarves she took out a month's lottery subscription that entitled her to a place in all draws or bonus games offered in that period. She put the ticket into the pocket of her mink coat when she got into the car.

She dropped Ellen off in front of the library on campus, hoping for a glimpse of Evan. She didn't see him, so she drove away.

When she reached home George was in the living room, hunched in the lounge near the fireplace. The flames leaped high on the hearth, spilled heat through the room in dry waves, but he, rolling a can of beer between his hands, looked as if he were chilled.

"Aren't you home early?" she asked.

He grunted.

"I had a nice lunch with Ellen at the club."

"And what did you give her this time?" he asked sourly.

"Nothing." The scarf didn't count. It was a small gift, not worth fighting about.

"I'll watch for that nothing on the bills at the end of the month."

"Oh, George," she sighed.

"I know you don't believe me. You can't. I don't want to myself. I can't believe it myself. But I'm not going to make it, Adelaide."

"Of course you will. All you have to do is hang on another month. Maybe even less. Then things will start moving. This is a bad time of year."

"That's what I keep telling myself."

"It's going to be all right, George."

"You don't know what you're talking about."

"Very well. I don't know. Then don't tell me your troubles. If I'm so stupid I can't understand, why worry me?"

"You have to be careful."

"I am. I have been ever since you began to say these awful things. But what else can I do?"

"Stay away from the club. Stay out of the shops." He drew a deep explosive breath. "Stop sending Evan the extra cash you're giving him."

Her face reddened. "And what about you?"

George didn't deny it. "You hear from him?"

"Not in the last few days."

"I don't want anybody to know, Adelaide. So watch your mouth. I mean it. Don't spread my troubles around."

She stared at him, confused, then realized that he'd switched from speaking of Evan to complaining about his own problems again.

"If the idea gets around that I'm broke, then I'll be sunk, Adelaide."

"I'm doing the best I can. And if you don't think I should go to the club, then I won't. But you know, if they don't see us there, people may start to wonder. Any change in our style will lead to suspicions."

She had started to leave the room when he said grudgingly, "Maybe you're right about that. Only be careful."

She kept on going.

Three miles away, in the State Lottery Commission's downtown office, Dorsey Dalton rolled an envelope into the typewriter and hit the keys at top speed. It was two minutes to five. She was determined to leave on time.

Moments later she shoved the off button, threw the gray cover over the machine. She grabbed her coat and sped through the door, calling, "Good night! See you tomorrow," well ahead of her co-workers. They were used to this, and knew about Bobsie, so they understood.

He was always on her mind. She couldn't help but talk about him. Most people were good. But not Henry Dalton. She always thought of him like that. Henry Dalton. His full name. If he'd had a middle initial, she'd have thought that, too. Her former husband. Bobsie's father.

Had she loved Henry Dalton once? She didn't remember. Did she miss him now that he was gone? No. No, she didn't miss him, or want him, or think of him in the long nights with any feeling beyond disgust.

Until Bobsie turned three months old, Dorsey had adored Henry Dalton. She had been the oldest of six, born in Pawtucket, Rhode Island, to a mill-working family. She'd had to go out on her own as soon as she finished high school. She married Henry Dalton two years later, and moved with him to St. Mary's City, expecting to live happily ever after. Until she heard him say, with a hard flush on his cheeks, "We never had anything like this in *my* family, Dorsey. What about you?"

Her arms had curled protectively around Bobsie, and she had answered, "I don't know. And neither do you. You heard what the doctor said."

"I don't believe everything I hear," Henry Dalton snapped.

For the next two weeks he had been silent, avoiding her, avoiding the sight of Bobsie. Then he'd said, packing his clothes, "I can't take it, Dorsey. I'm not going to."

She stared at him, speechless. Bobsie was his son, too. How could he turn his back on his baby boy?

Henry Dalton left. He sent a monthly check, which wasn't enough, so Dorsey went to work at the insurance company. She didn't make much, and paying Carrie Realin for babysitting Bobsie took most of it, but somehow, she had managed. The checks stopped coming after a year and a half. She hung on, struggling. When the lottery bill was passed, she went to work for the commission. It offered three dollars a week more, and a health plan. It was five years since she had seen Henry Dalton. She never expected to see him again.

She parked in front of Carrie's house, ran up the steps to knock, and threw the door open at the same time. The warmth, steaming, smelling of hot coffee and fresh bread, hit her just as Bobsie's wide-open and laughing grin hit her. He trotted to her on stubby legs, making his "Mama" sound. She caught him up, hugged him. "Bobsie, did you miss me?"

Carrie came from the kitchen. "He sure did. But he was good. He only cried a few minutes after you left."

Dorsey set the boy on his feet. "He's an armful."

"He eats like a dream," Carrie said. There was no envy in her tone, although her own Jill ate like a bird. Because of her own Jill, Carrie knew how Dorsey felt.

"Coffee's ready if you're willing to take a minute," Carrie was saying. "And fresh cinnamon bread for you to take along. Bobsie loves it."

The boy made his "cake" sound, laughed, hugged Dorsey's knees. She smiled at him. "I'll be there in a minute. I'll just go in and say hi to Jill."

"Watch her eyes," Carrie said. "See if she's looking at the door. I think she knows when to start waiting for you."

"It wouldn't surprise me," Dorsey answered. But when she went into the tiny bedroom, Jill's eyes were fixed dully on the ceiling.

Dorsey sighed, leaned over the crib to kiss Jill's bulging forehead.

"What do you think?" Carrie asked when Dorsey joined her at the kitchen table.

"I couldn't tell." It wasn't an outright lie, but it didn't completely destroy Carrie's hope. Dorsey didn't want to do that, yet she didn't want to encourage Carrie to be unrealistic. Jill was a hydrocephalic just as Bobsie was a mongoloid. The facts had to be faced, always, as long as they lived. She and Carrie had to deal with those facts, and use the real name for the conditions. But they had to have hope, too.

Carrie poured coffee, passed a slice of cinnamon bread to Dorsey, and held a second one toward Bobsie. When he reached for it, she drew it back. He hesitated, then yelled, "Cake." She turned to grin at Dorsey. "See?"

"He's close. With somebody trained, I know he could learn to talk." Dorsey sighed. "That Pennsylvania school—the one I heard about through the Association for Retarded Children." She'd written to find out the cost, feeling she had to try. Though it would be awful to send Bobsie away. It turned out that the tuition and board were far beyond her means. But they could teach Bobsie to speak, swim, ride a bus. Eventually he'd learn a simple trade. He could have a life. If only he could get to that school. To give him that much, she could bear the separation. But the money . . .

Carrie said, "I almost forgot. I bought our lottery ticket today." And then, with a grin: "You know, we're so silly."

"We're entitled to be." Dorsey took out two quarters. "My share."

They divided a ticket once a week. Dorsey couldn't play. That is, she could never win. Because she worked for the commission. Carrie couldn't afford a whole dollar a week. So, together, they gambled, laughing when they shook hands on the agreement to split between them whatever they won, if they ever did, while Carrie swore on Jill's health that she'd never admit to another human being that she was splitting with Dorsey Dalton, who was a clerk at the commission office.

They enjoyed deciding what they'd do with the proceeds, both certain they'd never be faced with the reality. Carrie said she'd enlarge her tiny house and set up a nice home for children like Jill and Bobsie. Dorsey always said she'd hire a special teacher so Bobsie could have the help he needed.

But now, smiling wryly, she said, "If we ever do win, I've decided. I'm going to send Bobsie to that school in Pennsylvania."

Carrie sighed, and Dorsey sighed. They looked at each other. At the same time, both women whispered, "Isn't it possible?" And: "Couldn't there be a way?" Then they sat back, staring into each other's eyes.

CHAPTER 11

Jerry Lakas leaned against the sedan fender, watching the back door of the Capitol Hotel. He didn't feel the cold wind that blew into his face. But when a sheet of weeks-old newspaper sailed down the alley and wrapped itself around his legs, he bent to pluck it away. A photograph caught his eye. A pretty girl. Young. With dark curly hair. The caption said her name was Mary Baker. It seemed familiar to him, though he didn't know why. Mary Baker. She had won fifty thousand dollars in the lottery and was going to buy a real house with it. Mary Baker, of the Riverton Trailer Park, in Riverton. He wondered why she was so lucky. Why she had everything: a husband, a home, a future. Why was she so lucky, when his Jenny was dead? The Riverton Trailer Park. One of these days, he told himself, he would be there. He would go and see Mary Baker.

But he forgot her as Quinn came out of the back door of the hotel and paused to settle her black beret more firmly.

The early morning sun seemed to her to be winking as clouds scudded before it and then passed on. She smiled, started briskly to the corner of the lot where she had left the Rabbit parked the night before.

Closer to it, her smile faded. The car squatted too close to the ground, and was almost afloat in the rustling blowing litter that surrounded it.

She broke into a run, snatched up some of the too familiar-looking debris. Order forms she had left locked in the hatch.

She saw quickly that the lock on the hatch was broken, then found that all four tires were slashed and flat.

She fought swift panic. First heat flooding her; then chill. It was foolish to assume that this, happening now in St. Mary's City, had anything to do with *A Friend*. Such things were common to people who worked on the road. It was only the first time for her. She had been due for it.

She hurried inside, reported what she had found to the desk clerk, and had him call a garage and the police.

An officer arrived first. He said, "There's been a rash of this kind of vandalism in Passamody. I guess it's spread here. That's how it goes. The radio, television . . . What can you do?"

"You think it's kids?"

"Most likely. But did you check to see if there's anything missing?"

"Nothing's been stolen. Everything is messed up, though."

"Kids then." He wrote laboriously in his notebook. "We'll keep our eyes open. That's all I can tell you."

The garage mechanic eyed the long knife cuts in the tires, shook his head. "Beats me that they'd pick on your little Rabbit. Usually it's a Cadillac."

Two hours later, leaving St. Mary's City, Quinn told herself that a crazy coincidence was assuming too much importance in her mind. She had to forget it, forget the letters, too.

But she was relieved when she arrived in Windsor and saw the twin towers of the Romanesque parish church and the simple spire of the Methodist church, both wreathed in low-hanging clouds.

A dusty tan sedan slowed behind her, then went on, as she turned into the Inland Motel driveway. She checked in at the desk. There was no message awaiting her from Michael. He'd said that he might be in Windsor that day, but wasn't sure. A small warmth swept her. It would be good if he did come. In her room she unpacked the dress she'd wear if she were to have a night out with him. She took down her hair, brushed it, and put it back up. She did her face. She was Quinn Monroe, she told herself. District manager for Becker's. In another few months she would be Quinn Monroe, setting out on a trip around the world. Someday soon she'd be walking the sandy shores of Tanzania, looking at the still blue waters of the Indian Ocean. She'd ferry to Zanzibar, and wander in the sisal and banana plantations, and maybe visit a diamond mine.

Primed by her daydreams, she left the motel.

By one thirty she had seen Elsa Martinelli, whose two daughters, a year apart, had colds, and screamed throughout the visit, while Elsa said apologetically, "My neighbor has her period and couldn't take them today." By then, too, Quinn had talked to Frances Bynam, who worked at the Central Public Library. The accounts of both women had been in perfect order, and both had earned bonuses for their sales.

Driving to her next stop, Quinn chose for Elsa a lace negligee, for Frances a warm woolly robe.

At the Roseview Home for the Elderly, settled in a back parlor, Quinn listened while Cherie LaBlanc said, "It's not that I want to quit, you understand." Her accent, usually much less French-Canadian, was stronger than Quinn had ever heard it, an indication that the woman was upset. "I cannot go on, seeing what I see, knowing what I know. I am the last of the old staff, but now I must go." Her shoulders drooped. "You may be able to deal with the new administrator. Mrs. Leggette is her name. But so far she says no one will be permitted to take over for me. She says the women don't need cosmetics. It's been terrible since Mrs. Westlake had to leave."

There was a commotion in the hallway, the sound of raised voices. One carried clearly above the others.

"I am not confined to a wheelchair. I never have been. I don't need one now. Just hand me my cane and I'll do as I please and go where I please."

"Mr. Gordon," Cherie whispered. "One of our residents."

Quinn smiled. "I've noticed him. He's a charmer."

"The new staff doesn't think so."

Immediately there followed proof of Cherie's statement.

"Now, Nathaniel, we mustn't be testy, must we?"

"*I* must," he answered. And: "I'm Mr. Gordon to you, Mrs. Bestow." Bastard, he thought.

"We must be gentle, must adjust, and realize that we're not all that we once were."

"*I* am," he said forcefully.

"Things have changed here, Mr. Gordon. We must be cooperative, or else we will be sorry."

"Then I guess you're going to be sorry, woman." It was better than trying to call her Mrs. Bestow. That could too easily turn into Bastard. Then the fat would be in the fire. He could imagine her saying, "We do not allow bad language, Nathaniel. Take this pill."

Quinn raised her brows, and Cherie said angrily, "You see? That's why I must leave here. And if I didn't, I would soon be fired."

"The residents will miss you."

"I cannot help it." Then: "Do you want to see Mrs. Leggette?" When Quinn nodded, Cherie led the way to the administrator's office, and went in. Within the moment, she returned. "Mrs. Leggette says to come another day. She's busy. But I am certain she has made up her mind to handle the selling of such things herself in Roseview."

Quinn took up her sample cases. "I'll come back in a few weeks.

Then we'll see." As Cherie walked her to the side door, they heard Nathaniel Gordon again.

He was saying angrily, "It's an outrage. A wheelchair when I don't need it. I won't put up with it!"

"He has no choice, poor man," Cherie whispered. "Unlike me, he cannot go away." When she had waved Quinn off, Cherie went into the hall.

Nathaniel was seated in his wheelchair. His hands were folded in his lap. His face was pink with anger. His bright blue eyes were fixed balefully on his cane, which hung just out of his reach on the banister. He was seventy-seven years old, small and spare, with white hair and thick white brows.

He shifted his gaze from the cane to Cherie's face. "You're leaving." It wasn't a question. Roseview had its grapevine. It was often inaccurate, but always fast. Very little that happened there went undiscussed.

"I must go," Cherie said.

"I don't blame you. It'll be bad, seeing how it was before, and what the place has become."

"Maybe it'll be better than you think, Mr. Gordon."

"Don't try to cheer me up. Have you seen the rules?" He went on bitterly, "No television after eight o'clock at night. No late news. The best shows gone." He threw up his gnarled hands. "It's no use. It won't be any good."

The worst was he couldn't leave. He'd turned over all his small assets in exchange for lifetime care. He had enough Social Security for pocket money. It wouldn't pay for rent and food. He had no children to go to. It was the same for the others at Roseview. When Beth Westlake had to sell Roseview, the lifetime contracts went along with the building and furniture. But National Nursing Homes Company had the right to make its own rules.

Cherie wasn't afraid of Mrs. Leggette anymore. She unhooked his cane from the banister, put it within his reach. He snatched it, gave her a sweet smile, and rolled away.

In the room that had been home for twelve years, he used the cane to lever himself out of the chair. He sent it spinning with a contemptuous grunt. Until the new owners took over, the room had been a pleasant sanctuary for two men. Now it held four, with furniture to accommodate them, and no space in which an angry man could pace.

At the moment, he had privacy. The others were watching television, absorbing the outside world from children's cartoons and women's soap operas. Nathaniel's face hardened. A man needed to see the news at six, at eleven. To watch the after-nine specials.

He limped in a small circle, passing the window that faced on the back yard. Shadows streaked the melting snow with pale ribbons. The trees were still black and gaunt. By summer they would be leafy and full. He wondered briefly if he would see them that way, and decided he would. He'd already turned seventy-seven. Why not seventy-eight? The question was where he would be by then.

Not here in Roseview. He, unlike so many of the others, was fortunate to have his health. His weakened left leg hardly slowed him down, though it did make the cane necessary. He could still be useful, and though he hadn't seen them for a while, he certainly had friends remaining in town.

He limped to the table in which his few belongings were stored. Razor, hair brush, tooth brush, denture powder. Two ties, two shirts, an extra pair of trousers. As little as it was, it was too much for him to carry. He found a paper bag, put in shaving articles and one shirt. He'd send for the rest when he was settled.

Bundled in his only sweater, his old winter coat buttoned firmly, he walked quickly and proudly outside. Goodbye, Mrs. Bestow. Bastard. Goodbye, Mrs. Smithy. Smutty.

A gray mist hovered over the road. He limped down the highway in the direction of Windsor. He knew every inch of the two miles. Until Beth Westlake had had to give up, there had been twice weekly trips into town for those who could make them. Roseview, then, had been a *home* for the elderly. Bless Beth Westlake. And damn the misfortune that had come upon her! Her husband, Gentry, had been a young man of fifty-one. A big, fast-moving strong young man, with the patience of a saint who had eternity ahead of him in which to do his chores. Suddenly Gentry had begun to move slow, then slower. His bigness shrank away. His ruddy face grayed. He went to bed one day and never rose again. Beth Westlake nursed him, ran the home, smiling while she held death at bay. For Gentry, for some of the others, too. She fought as long as she could, but she lost Gentry. She tried to keep going, but at the end it was the same as it had been with Nathaniel himself. The illness had taken all she had. She was forced to sell Roseview to NNHC. She was gone now to a town in the South, to work for someone else.

Nathaniel blinked away gray mists and stumbled on. He passed a fairly new house, disapproved of the materials put into it. He knew unseasoned lumber and poor hardware. He'd owned a building-supply store until his stroke. When he finally had to give the business up, it hadn't brought much. That plus his cashed-in life insurance had gone to Roseview for lifetime care. Except for that stroke, though, he'd still be living on his own as he had done since his wife Minerva's death at forty-nine.

Again he blinked away gray mists. He paused to rest, leaning on his cane, before he went on.

It took him over two hours to reach the vacant store that had once been his. He stopped to look. Its windows were boarded. A sign was in tatters. The place had been abandoned. He shook his head sadly as he turned away.

When he entered the drugstore he knew something was wrong. A stranger stood behind the counter where young Doc Roseman should have been. When Nathaniel asked, the man said, "Dr. Roseman retired and sold out," And: "How can I help you?"

Nathaniel considered, but didn't say. Young Doc would very likely have tried to dissuade him, but would have given in in the end. He'd know at least that Nathaniel could sell cigars and cigarettes and camera film as well as the next man. This stranger would only laugh.

Nathaniel went into the street. He made his planned rounds slowly, but with diminishing confidence. At the neighborhood store where he once shopped regularly, and which was not his last stop, all was welcome and friendliness. But when he mentioned a job, Harry Taylor simply shook his bald head. "Can't do it, Nathaniel, though I'd like to. We don't have enough coming in to pay you. Be glad you've got a roof over your head and a warm bed these cold nights."

He pressed a ham sandwich on Nathaniel, a pint of milk. In return, Nathaniel bought a lottery ticket, grinning, "Something pleasant to look forward to." He made a big fuss about choosing what game he wanted, determined to make Harry believe he really wanted one. No. He wouldn't play hockey, nor match money. No, he didn't care for the idea of the new one, galaxies, in which you had to choose a particular star. He finally settled on a number in the jackpot draw.

Before he left, he asked casually who had taken over the old building in which he had once had his store. Harry told him the bank had it now. Nobody else would touch it.

On the street again Nathaniel reflected that his afternoon snack had been better than what he'd have had at Roseview, where, he supposed, along about now they'd have discovered he was gone. The snack would have been a single graham cracker, a cup of weak tea. Nathaniel calculated that since NNHC had taken over it had already managed to reduce costs by half.

He made two more stops, refusing to be discouraged even though he knew it wasn't going to be any good. There just wasn't anyplace for a seventy-seven-year-old man who wanted to be on his own.

Finally tired, without any more ideas, he wandered past his old store. Obviously it had been vacant a long while. And there was the room at the back. It had a single window, much too high for anyone to peer into. Covered, it wouldn't give off noticeable light. A kerosene camper's light, a cot, a spirit stove . . . Nathaniel grinned happily.

He had a rent-free room. He was considering how to break into the building when he remembered his Social Security check. It wasn't much, and not enough to live on, but it would buy his food. He needed it, and an address at which it could be delivered. It couldn't come to an abandoned building.

This required some thinking about. But he was beginning to feel a dangerous numbness in his feet, an ache in his throat, a small stinging in his temples. He turned, thinking to go back to Harry Taylor's to rest. A gust of wind lashed at him from around the corner. It caught him, flung him into the wall. He hung there, gasping, blinded by sudden tears.

That was when Quinn saw him. She hesitated, half in the car, half out, after her last stop of the day. An old man, nearly blown off his feet . . .

She crossed the road at a trot. Drawing closer, she recognized him. Another gust caught him, half turned his body, tore at his coat.

She took a firm grip on his arm. "You're Mr. Gordon, aren't you?"

He gasped an acknowledgment, peered at her through wind-watering blue eyes.

"I'm Quinn Monroe," she explained. "I was at Roseview earlier today to see Cherie LaBlanc."

He smiled. "She sells Becker's for you. It makes the ladies feel good to wear that junk."

"Let me give you a lift," Quinn said, drawing him toward the Rabbit. "It'll be dark soon. And it's too cold to be walking."

He went with her. A ride would be good. It would let him rest. He must decide what to do. Damn the government! Why did a check have to be mailed to an address? There ought to be an easier way. He'd have to find out. And until then . . .

"You're going back to Roseview, aren't you?" she was asking.

He hesitated. But where else was there? Before he did anything, he had to know about the check. Then he had to get the back room ready. One day soon, he'd move himself in, and be on his own. He answered gruffly, "I guess I am. What about you?"

"I'm in no hurry," she answered, thinking of Michael. If he were coming, he'd have arrived by now. Her hunger to see him frightened her. She'd told him he couldn't change her. But it was happening, even as she willed it not to. Then a picture flickered in her mind of the Rabbit's knife-cut tires . . . the rustling pink order blanks. She wouldn't tell him about what had happened that morning. He'd say what the policeman had said, the garage mechanic, too. *A rash of vandalism to cars.* And maybe that's all it was.

With a sigh, Nathaniel settled himself, his hands clasped on his cane, his paper bag tucked between his knees.

"Roseview's changed a lot," Quinn said. "I wonder if there's anything to be done."

Nathaniel laughed bitterly. "If there is, I don't know it. Every resident there put in what he had, on the promise of care and a home for as long as he lived. When Beth Westlake sold, that was part of the contract. But the new people have their own rules. And when I complain, they tell me I'm senile."

She gave him a brief look. "Nobody could say that about you, Mr. Gordon."

"Anybody can say anything about anybody. And get away with it, too. Besides, not many listen to a man my age."

"What about your family?" she asked.

"Nobody's left."

It was the same for her, Quinn thought. That was how things were. People always ended up alone. Distance, time, life itself broke all bonds eventually. Michael could curse it, but that was how it was.

A moment's silence. Sadness. She clicked on the radio to dispel it. ". . . two-hour wait, law-enforcement officials dispersed, saying they had had a bad tip," the newscaster said. "Drug sales investigation will go forward, however." And: "A general warming trend, with chance of snow flurries tonight. Tides at normal on the coast."

As she switched off the radio, Nathaniel chuckled. "Back in the twenties it was whiskey. The bootleggers'd send somebody to a coastal town like Jewell's Landing or Saugatuck Island. He'd buy a house and dock. And business would proceed." He grinned at her. "The drug people are doing the same, I bet you. But try to make anybody listen."

She thought of the trooper named Lacy Pickett in the Elkhorn substation. She had tried to make him listen. She knew what Nathaniel meant.

Ahead, she saw the lights of Roseview.

Nathaniel saw them, too. He said quickly, "Listen, you're so young you maybe wouldn't know about Social Security. But in case you do . . . I was wondering if there's some way to have the check mailed to someplace besides your home address."

"I'll find out," she said. "I'll let you know."

She slowed, stopped in the curved drive.

He sighed. It was a discouragement to look on the place. All he could think of was escape. A spirit lamp, a cot. He'd have his own little home. He'd miss the television and the radio and the company, too. But at least he'd be certain he wouldn't end up in a nightgown split down the back, or hogtied into a wheelchair. And if he ate beans, they'd be his own canned beans, and not counted onto his plate as if they belonged to someone else.

He thanked her for the ride, said he hoped he'd see her again, and watched until she had driven away. There was nothing he liked more than a pretty woman, he thought as he went inside.

"Mr. Gordon!" The words were sharp, tossed at him like pebbles. "Where have you been?"

He removed his hat and coat, and held them, leaning on his cane. That great cow, Mrs. Leggette, stood before him. He considered how much he disliked large stout females, saying, "I went on an errand."

"But where? What do you mean by doing such a thing?"

He said coldly, "I don't like your tone, young lady."

She should have enjoyed the compliment. She was fifty-five if she was a day. Young to him maybe. But to whom else?

She ignored it. She said, "You're not in condition to traipse about alone. We feared you were lost."

"Only because you'd have to look for me."

"Mr. Gordon, if you don't like it here—"

"You've told me."

"Then we understand each other?"

"I don't believe we do. But I don't believe we ever will either."

"There are rules. You cannot ignore them."

"This isn't a training school nor a penal institution."

She glared at him over a forced smile. "We must try to get along, Mr. Gordon. This contention can't be good for your arteries."

"You worry about your arteries. I'll take care of mine." He turned to go to his room.

"Supper at six," Mrs. Leggette said.

"The news is at six," he answered, and limped to the stairs.

CHAPTER 12

There was a message awaiting Quinn when-she finally returned to the Inland Motel. Michael had phoned to say he wouldn't be able to get to Windsor.

She sighed, put away the green dress she had unpacked that morning. She busied herself with some phone calls. On the last of them, she learned that a Social Security check could be deposited directly to the recipient's bank if he wished. She decided to tell Nathaniel that the next day.

But when she asked for him at Roseview, she was told that he wasn't well and was keeping to his bed. After repeated demands and heated insistence, she was finally taken upstairs.

His room was underheated and overcrowded. Four pairs of eyes fixed on her as she hesitated on the threshold.

Nathaniel looked, blinked, and rose from the edge of the bed where he had been huddling. "I can't offer you a chair because they took mine away. Shall we go down to the sitting room?" Without waiting, he limped ahead.

The sitting room, too, was underheated, but the sun was bright.

Quinn thought the old man seemed tired. When she asked him, he said, "Angry. That's what I am. It was either stay put up there or find myself stuck in bed and tranquilized with pills." His blue eyes met her questioning look. "They didn't like my going to town without announcing it."

"About your check," Quinn said. "All you need to do is go to your bank and fill out a form. Then it'll be mailed there."

He thanked her, then asked if she were returning to Windsor. When she said she was, he got to his feet. "If you don't mind giving me a ride again, I'll go to the bank right now."

"But what about Mrs. Bestow?"

"Leave her to me," he grinned.

He got his coat and hat. This time he didn't take anything else with him. He already knew he'd have to be patient a little longer. Just long enough to be sure that he had an account at the bank, that his check had been received there. He limped into Mrs. Leggette's office and informed her that he was going on a small errand with Miss Monroe.

"An errand?" the administrator asked suspiciously.

"That's right." And forestalling the next question: "She's going to bring me back, too."

He had every intention of walking back, but, when they reached the bank, Quinn insisted on waiting while he went in to inquire and to make the arrangements. He was about to leave when a middle-aged man stopped him.

"Mr. Gordon? Don't you remember me? I'm Tom Galt. Used to be called Tommy. I often came into your store with my father."

Nathaniel grinned, shook hands, faintly recalling a young smiling face, a blond cowlick of impressive proportions.

"And what are you doing here?" Tom Galt asked. There was no cowlick now, and little rivers of pink scalp showed between strands of blondish gray hair.

Nathaniel explained, asked what Tommy did in the bank.

"I'm one of the two V.P.'s," Tommy said. "My father's retired."

Nathaniel recalled that his old building was held by the bank, according to Harry Taylor, the grocer. Nathaniel decided to say nothing about that.

Tommy Galt pumped his hand. "Mr. Gordon, if you need any help, you just come to me."

Nathaniel returned to the Rabbit, smiling in satisfaction. Yes. He'd been rightly informed by Quinn. He'd signed a form, then two others. It might take a month, maybe even two, but then his checks would be deposited for him at the bank. He'd even arranged to stop by to pick up the deposit notification. And further, he'd run into a friend from the old days.

Quinn asked if he had anything else he'd like to do, but he thanked her, shook his head.

After she dropped him off at Roseview, she returned to Windsor. A dusty tan sedan was two cars behind her when she had finished up there and set out for Ballston.

Friday evening. Elkhorn.

Quinn held her breath as she went through the mail. Travel information. Three bills. A note from the regional manager congratulating her on the previous months' sales and enclosing a small bonus.

There was nothing else.

She let out her breath on a gust of relieved laughter.

A Friend had finally given up. It was over. And the knife-cut tires in St. Mary's City had only been random vandalism after all.

CHAPTER 13

"For a man recuperating, you do travel around a lot," Mrs. Varnick said.

Jerry smiled faintly, peered at her through his steel-rimmed glasses. "I like to see the countryside. It's pretty, and different from Kansas."

"But you feel better, don't you?"

"I do. This is really what I've needed for a long time."

Later that day Mrs. Varnick said sadly to May, who was bagging the small grocery purchases, "I'm afraid my Mr. Lakes is going back to Kansas, where he comes from, pretty soon. He says he's recovering from his illness. And he certainly acts it, hopping into his car all the time and driving away."

"Don't worry," May reassured the old lady. "In another month the summer people will be coming in. Somebody'll turn up." And that night she told her sister Eva Pickett to start keeping an ear out for someone who might want a room at Mrs. Varnick's, because the old lady thought her man would be leaving for his home in Kansas any time. Eva promised she would, and that night, as she and her state trooper husband were going to bed, she said, "Mrs. Varnick's roomer's probably going back to Kansas, so if you hear of anybody who wants a place send him to her." But Lacy, his hands curled around Eva's full breasts, wasn't listening.

When Jerry left Mrs. Varnick, he went up to his room. He took off his parka and cap and hung them neatly away. He loosened his shirt and eased the buckle of the money belt he had worn since he left Kansas City. Standing at the window, he looked down on the Old North Road, the neglected yard where he had left his car.

This, being here, yes, that was what he had needed for a long seven years. Once again he felt close to Jenny. Because he was close to Quinn, who had lived with Jenny and known her.

He put his transistor on the table near his bed and lay down, thinking that things happened exactly as they had to. When events occurred it was the way they were meant to be.

All those years of waiting, hungering . . . nothing.

Then, a summer day. The doorbell rang. He was on the threshold nearly, about to go out. He pulled the door open. The postman muttered something about the weather and thrust the mail at him. Jerry almost didn't see the long envelope with Jenny's name on it. Something was stuck on top. He dropped that, and then, staring at him: "Miss Jennifer Lakas." In red ink there was written the name of her college. Her home address was scrawled over it in blue.

He shoved it under his shirt, took the other mail into the kitchen, and went outside.

Hiding in the car, he studied the envelope again. The return address was Internal Revenue Service. He supposed it was an old tax bill. He tore it open. A twenty-dollar check was enclosed. A refund from three years before. An error in withholding. The job had been in Washington, D.C. The notice had been sent first there, forwarded to the nursing school in Chicago, then directed to the college, and had finally been addressed to the house in Kenyon.

Jenny was, or had been, in Washington, D.C., some three years earlier.

For two full days he lay on his bed, waiting. The transistor played softly beside him. Country music. The words of his love and loss. About finally coming together again.

Then, while his parents slept, he set out for Washington.

It took him two days of driving through sun-scorched landscapes, through baking cities. It took him ten days of patient waiting. He didn't eat, but he wasn't hungry. He didn't sleep, but he never tired. He knew he would find her. He did.

Three o'clock. She came out through the wide glass door that slid open when she stepped in front of it. Sun blinded him. Or perhaps it was tears. When he was able to look again, she was in a blue convertible. Her face was just as he remembered it. Not from when he had seen her last, but as she had been as a child. She was laughing. The wind tousled her chestnut hair. The driver smoothed curls from her cheek as he edged the car into the stream of traffic at the circle.

It was easy to keep them in sight. The light head and the chestnut one were close together, separating only when the convertible pulled up and double-parked before the tall white building, and Jenny got out.

Jerry double-parked, too, but around the corner. After Jenny had disappeared inside, he ambled along the sidewalk. The convertible had an M.D. on its bumper. A stethoscope tossed carelessly into the back seat glinted in the sun. The man behind the wheel had thick blond curly hair and long sideburns. His shirt was white and silky-looking. The blue flaring tie he wore was loosened at his tanned throat.

Jerry went to the corner, teetered on the curb and started back. When Jenny emerged from the building, she carried a weekend case. Jerry saw it, even though he was down on one knee tying a shoelace that didn't need it. He had gone to the trouble for no purpose. She hadn't even glanced his way. Her eyes were only for the man in the convertible.

Jerry caught up with them at the corner and followed them into the left-turn lane, and then into Wisconsin Avenue. He drove, losing track of time and mileage, the radio alternating between rock music and news about local muggings. He noticed nothing along the way.

When the convertible swung into the motel parking lot, he went after it at a discreet distance.

He sat in his car, drowsing. Jenny belonged to him, and always had, and always would.

Hours later they appeared again. Once more he followed them. The convertible stopped to let Jenny out at her building, and went on.

Jerry went on, too. He was half a block away when it turned into a driveway. He watched the tall blond man enter the long low house.

Jerry waited. He sat empty-minded and empty-handed. He thought nothing, planned nothing. He stared at the driveway that led to the garage. It was lined with thick shielding shrubs and bordered with flower beds behind brick dividers.

At eight o'clock the blond man came out of the house. A small blond woman was with him.

Jerry didn't follow when they drove away.

It was midnight when the couple returned. By then Jerry's car was two blocks down the road, but Jerry was standing in the thick shrubbery near the garage.

He smelled the scent of the small blond woman as she passed him by. He heard the bitterness of her voice, saying, "We could have stayed another hour. It wouldn't have killed you," as she flounced into the house. He listened to the explosive bang of the door as it slammed shut behind her.

The blond man swore quietly. He took the stethoscope from the back seat of the convertible, and then came on.

Jerry stepped from the shrubbery.

The man stopped, a smile beginning on his lips.

"She belongs to me," Jerry whispered.

The beginning of the smile was gone. "Who are you? What do you want?"

"She belongs to me," Jerry repeated. He swung the brick in two swift crushing blows, leaping back as the man went down, sprawled and silent.

Jerry jerked the coat back over the wide shoulders, slid a thick wallet from a hip pocket, and disappeared into the shadow-shrouded street. It had taken only a moment.

The next morning it was on the first page of the *Washington Post*. Tilman Downer, the noted surgeon on the staff of the George Washington University Hospital, had been mugged virtually on his doorstep and was found dead of head wounds by his wife, thirty-three-year-old Lucinda. There followed a brief rundown of the four other prominent victims of street crimes, none of whom had succumbed to their injuries, but all of whom had been assaulted within the past six weeks.

Jerry gave the item a quick reading before he threw the paper away. He looked at his watch, looked at the hospital doorway. Moments after three, Jenny appeared.

He could tell that she knew. Her face was white, her mouth sucked in, as if the inner lip were caught between her teeth. She walked with a stiff slow uneven gait.

He waited until she had reached the sidewalk, then he stepped from behind the thick trunk of the tree. He stood squarely before her. "Jenny."

She stopped with a lurch and a stagger. Her white face became even whiter. Her eyes were suddenly wide, staring. "It's you," she whispered, her hands reaching unwillingly to touch him, then pulling back to clench at her sides.

"You didn't have to run away," he said quietly.

"You," she said again. "It's you, isn't it? Til . . . last night . . ."

Jerry shook his head. No one had seen him. The wallet was gone into the Potomac River. He'd done nothing but find his Jenny again.

"Like before," she whispered. "That time . . . when I was in school . . . when I left . . . and now . . ."

"I just wanted to find you, Jenny."

"Why? Why? Why couldn't you leave me alone? Did you think it was easy for me? Do you think I didn't remember, and need you, and dream of you?"

"You belong to me, Jenny."

"Wrong. Wicked. It always was. We both knew it. We sinned so terribly, Jerry. I couldn't live with it. I couldn't. Won't you understand?"

"I need you," he said softly.

"No, Jerry. All these years, I've fought it. I hurt Ma and Pa so much, going away, never writing, because if I did, you'd know. You'd find me. And maybe I couldn't be strong enough—"

"You aren't."

"Go away from me, Jerry."

The old words.

"I never want to see you again."

More old words.

Scenes whipped through his mind. Flashes on a bright screen, with her face glaring palely from beyond it.

The boy, slim, golden-haired. Jenny, looking up at him with adoration in her eyes. The two always together. And where they went, he went behind them. Days, nights . . . always Jenny turned on him, eyes flashing. "Go away, Jerry. Go home. You're my brother, and that's how it'll always be. Just leave me alone. You don't belong here, Jerry!"

A pretense of acceptance—a farewell at which she wept but hid her tears . . . Silence and hunger for six endless days. He emerged from those days by dark to stand unseen at her door. He was there when she opened it to the golden-haired boy, and saw her arms tighten around the slim hard body. The door closed. Later all the lights went out. He could still see what happened within.

The two bodies forming one. Legs entwined, hips rising. A sheen of sweat on back and shoulders. A blinding sheen that sent him reeling away with the knowledge that Jenny had found surcease from anguish but that he never could . . .

The golden-haired boy stopped because he had to. There was no way for him to go with Jerry's car angled across the road.

He came out, swearing.

Jerry let him get close, then swung the jack handle. The boy screamed and fell back. Jerry struck again and again.

He took the boy's wallet, turned the pockets inside out, moved his car to the road shoulder, and drove off, thinking that the radio's occasional warnings against hitchhiking pickups were right. It was a dangerous business to stop a car for a stranger.

The next morning Jenny stared at him. Her eyes bright with terror. Her voice hating. "You killed Ricky," she screamed. "You did it, Jerry. Go away from me. I never want to see you again."

When Jerry reached to touch her, she shrank with loathing, and fled.

She finished school at the end of the term. She never came home, never wrote. A day after she received her diploma she disappeared.

Now she stood before him, shaking. "You, Jerry—last night—Til. And years ago, Ricky, too—" Her voice was shrill, hysterical: sobs and gasps punctuated the words. "We share the guilt between us. You. Me. We've always been in it together. But it can't be, Jerry. It can't."

"No," he said softly. "No, Jenny, you're wrong. You always were. You can't fight what has to be. I want you to come home with me. You belong with me."

"Oh, God," she screamed. "Oh, God, no, no—" She covered her face and stumbled away, followed by curious looks and the whispers of passersby.

He went after her, but she threw herself into a cab. She was gone before he could do anything to stop her.

It took him time to find the apartment building to which he had followed her the day before. There was no place to park nearby, so he left the sedan a block away and walked.

He heard sirens, saw blinking lights. He was there on the sidewalk when the ambulance arrived, and the police cars. Soon passing tenants mentioned Jenny Lakas. Later, in the lobby, he saw a tall slender girl with red-gold hair walk between two policemen toward an elevator door, and heard the whisper of her name for the first time. Quinn Monroe.

He was back in Kenyon when the call came from the Montgomery County police. He heard his mother scream, his father make the arrangements. He went with them when Jenny was buried.

He read the note from Quinn Monroe, and saw the clothes unpacked and hastily put away. He noticed the pretty ring and earclips, and hid them with the pictures of young Jenny.

Then he read Quinn Monroe's name again. She had luck on her side. Good fortune trailed her, as though Jenny had never died.

He wished her well, and wrote her so, but as the days passed an itch began in him. He had to see her, to know her, to understand why she was alive.

Kenyon, Kansas, to Kansas City, Missouri. The bank where he kept his money. The pawnshop where he had learned that the pretty ring and earclips were diamonds. Dr. Downer had been wealthy enough to give Jenny expensive presents.

On Route 70 East. Jefferson City. St. Louis. Indianapolis to Route 65 North, the Ohio Turnpike and Cleveland. And then due east, to Passamody and Elkhorn. To Quinn Monroe, who lived on, in joy, after Jenny died.

He knew the girl now; the weekend Quinn wore her hair on her shoulders, so it glowed in the sun, and the weekday Quinn looked like a model out of a magazine ad. He had followed her many times to Windsor and St. Mary's City. He had slept in the room next to hers in Ballston. He had trailed her down the streets of Riverton, where the other lucky one lived, pretty Mary Baker, who had everything, too. Just as Quinn did.

He had ridden Old Barn Road and turned around in the yard in front of the house Quinn lived in, and seen the black cat stalk a crow along the top of the stone fence. He had found the house beyond the hill across the meadow, and driven the dirt trail that led to it from Westbrook Road.

He had stood on her doorstep and asked the older woman who lived with Quinn for directions, and watched her bedroom lights go out on weekend nights.

She lived, and had everything. All the lucky people—they had everything. It could have been that way for Jenny, too. But Jenny died.

It wasn't right for it to be that way. It wasn't right.

He turned his chestnut head and wept into his pillow.

CHAPTER 14

Sunday. April first, April Fools' Day.

Of winter's snow there was left only narrowing veins in shaded ravines. But the meadows were still brown and gray, and the air was cold.

Michael drove too fast over the ruts on Old Barn Road, swung into the yard, and jammed on his brakes beside the Rabbit. He got out, banging the door behind him.

The night before had been good: he and Quinn in front of the fire . . . her head on his shoulder . . . She had spoken of her trip, said, smiling, "I'll make the reservations soon. First, two weeks in San Francisco. For June first."

"Make it the fifteenth, and maybe I can go with you," he'd told her.

She'd raised her eyes to his. "Michael! Are you serious?"

"If I can finish the book in time."

But then her glance slanted away. "I don't know—"

"The fifteenth, Quinn. I mean it."

"All right," she'd said. "I promise."

He'd thought he'd won at last.

Now he knew how wrong he'd been. Only moments before he'd been at Sears' garage.

Bill had said, "Hear your girl had some trouble, Mike."

Michael had assumed Bill was referring to the letters, unsurprised that Bill had heard of them. Bill heard everything. Then Michael reminded himself there'd been no more letters.

Bill had gone on, "Four tires, and the hatchback lock."

"What're you talking about?" Michael had demanded.

"Didn't you know? It happened upstate someplace. She didn't mention it. Only I know the Rabbit. She had the four new tires, and the new lock. So I asked her."

"And . . . ?"

"She didn't tell me much." Bill had grinned. "She's a pretty cool customer. But I guess you know."

Michael drove away in a fog of rage. Why was he doing this to himself? Why didn't he let her go, forget her? She would go just so far and then pull back. When he felt sure of her, he found he had lost her. And what was the matter? Why hadn't she told him? The letters had frightened her. This must have frightened her even more. His own intuition of real trouble ahead was part of his anger.

He started for the door, determined to have it out with her. To settle it once and for all.

When he reached the step, the door opened. Quinn smiled at him. She wore a heavy blue sweater, the sleeves pushed up to the elbow, and dark trousers, and her hair was loose on her shoulders. The sight of her, the hunger that rose in him, made him even angrier.

"Hi, Michael," she said, and bent to pick up a long white florist's box that he hadn't noticed on the stoop. It had an elaborate purple bow on which a tiny envelope rode like a pink butterfly.

He told himself to go about it calmly. Just to ask her what had happened. The first words he said were a rough "What the hell's the matter with you, Quinn?"

Her smile faltered. She hugged the box to her as if it were armor. "What do you mean, Michael? Is something wrong?"

"Bill Sears just told me about your tires."

"Oh," she said. "Oh, that." She bent her head over the box, untied the bow, and looped it over her arm.

"Why didn't you tell me yourself?" he demanded.

"There was nothing to tell." The sheaf of her hair hid her face. "I reported it. The police say it's happened before. Just one of those things."

"And you didn't think it worth mentioning? You didn't think I'd be interested?"

"Stop shouting," she said coolly.

"I've got to."

She shrugged, lifted the cover from the box.

She gasped, her lips suddenly gray. Before she could prevent it, a wail of anguish burst from her throat.

Michael reached for her, and for the box at the same time.

Devil, the black cat, lay within, staring. His pointed ears were flat. His triangular head was turned at a terrible angle.

Helen crowded into the doorway, whimpering. Michael thrust the box at her, led Quinn inside. He put her into a chair, held to her pale lips the brandy Helen brought on the run.

Quinn sipped it slowly. The color came back to her mouth. "Poor Devil," she whispered dully.

One more part of her life destroyed. She lay her head against the back of the chair, closed her eyes. The letters which had wished her well, but frightened her. The knife-cut tires. Now Devil . . .

She knew what Michael would say. The letters had stopped coming. Kids had been vandalizing cars all over the state. Dogs and cats had been killed in a northern county. There was no dark thing hanging over her. There was no reason for her to be afraid.

Helen said quietly, "If you don't need me . . ."

Quinn shook her head.

Michael answered, "No. It's okay now."

He took a good long look at the white florist's box Helen carried with her when she left.

He knew the shop in Passamody. They must sell flowers to fit such boxes by the dozen every day. But just to be certain, he would check.

When he spoke, he surprised Quinn. He didn't remind her that animals had been killed in the northern part of the state. "It's ugly," he said quietly. "And I don't like it. And coming after the letters—"

"You don't think I'm crazy then?"

He shook his head. "No. There's something." But he wanted to reassure her, to wipe the fear and revulsion from her face. At the same time, he knew he had to find a way to protect her. His hand tightened around her fingers. "I was mad as hell at you before."

She smiled faintly. "I remember."

"I still am. I want you to learn to share with me. Not hide from me. I want you to let yourself understand how much you matter to me." He waited. Then: "And how much I matter to you."

Helen came in at that moment. She put a small white kitten on Quinn's lap. "I got her at Fieldstone's, and if you don't like her, they'll take her back."

Michael held his breath while Quinn looked down at the kitten. If she refused it, she was refusing him, love, the future.

After a moment's silence, she smiled faintly, and whispered, "Hi, Snowball," taking the warm fluffy body into her arms.

The caution light blinked yellow and Quinn slowed, frowning at the car that was following too close behind her. As she went on through, she peered into the rearview mirror. She saw nothing but the brilliance of blinding light behind her.

It was a foggy evening in Jewell's Landing, with visibility poor, and foghorns wailing in the cove, and buoy beacons swinging to lead the fishing boats safely in. She was relieved to turn into the alley that led to the parking lot of the Landing Motel.

All day, as she made her stops, she had thought of the April Fools' Day gift left on her doorstep. All day, in spite of herself, she had wondered what would happen next.

Sighing, she parked the car, locked the passenger-side door, then felt the seat for her gloves. They were good ones, tan suede with fur lining. She didn't find them on the seat. They weren't on the floor, nor in the hatch with her sample cases. She checked her pockets. No. She'd had them that morning, and she'd need them. The nights were still very cold. She started the car and drove to Farkas' Emporium.

Her thoughts turned inward, she nodded thanks and passed through the door held open by a tall Indian.

He watched her go on, thinking that he'd give a lot to climb on top of her and forget his worries in a good long screw.

His name was Joe Nighthawk. In his middle fifties, he had a thick head of black hair. His high-cheekboned face was wind-weathered. He had been a fisherman all his life, and his hands were pocked with small scars, some purple, some welted pink.

He had just left the store, where he'd learned he couldn't buy a christening gown for his daughter's first child. He'd wasted half the day without finding the right one at the right price.

His daughter liked flashy. Only her fat-ass husband never worked steady. Always running up to a fucking meeting at St. Mary's City to yell about some fool fucking thing.

Now Joe stamped away from the door. Goddamn! It all cost too much. And a man couldn't get enough odd jobs this month. And with the fucking boat gone, fishing was out. Even if you could make a living at it by cutting every corner.

He got into his pickup. He kicked the starter. Nothing happened. "Oh, shit! You go, you pig-headed prick!" He tried again. That time it caught.

Jesus, Mary, and Joseph! He maneuvered out of the parking lot, thinking about the boat again, and how to get it fixed.

He rolled the window down, spat into the cold air. And what would he tell Geraldine when he got home? No loan at the bank. Joe was sure it was the goddamn land claims suit. He could read the lousy white-eyes' mind. "Stinking Indian . . . going to get half the state, and in here begging three thousand off me."

It was the same everywhere. He could smell it like rot rising in a swamp. Hatred. Suspicion. Because of the suit.

Joe spat again. He'd seen an ad. Forty-foot lobster boat for sale. Six thousand. And three, no matter how he figured, to repair his own.

Ahead he saw the turn-off for the house. Geraldine would run to meet him, eyes searching his face. She'd know he'd wasted his time.

More than anything just then he wanted to get his hands on Geraldine's ass. Not now, no way.

He passed the turn-off. He had eight dollars in his pocket. He swung into Henley's Bar.

The early crowd was there. Redheaded Pogie, who was single; Nick the Greek, who always had money; Frenchy, who lived down the road from Joe.

They greeted him, and he made himself a part of the group as somebody let out a whoop of glee, yelling, "Five dollars! What do you know!"

"You'd think he'd buy a round for the house," Pogie complained as the man collected his money and left.

The bartender shook his head. "An outsider just passing through."

Joe sipped his beer, trying to make it last. It was gone too soon. What the hell! He had another. It went down goddamn fast. He decided to leave.

Pogie tried to stop him. Nick the Greek asked how he was doing. Frenchy grinned at him. Joe got himself away.

But he stopped, bought himself an instant-win lottery ticket. Hockey game. Match the score. He didn't. Another fifty cents blown to hell.

Only you never knew, he told himself. He shrugged, went out. He *did so* know. He wasn't a winner. Never would be.

Now if he could just get his hands inside Geraldine's pants . . .

He spat before he got into the pickup. It was sure as hell time to go home.

That day Michael had an appointment in Pikesville, a suburb of Baltimore. He was supposed to be on a flight out of Passamody at 10:04, to catch a plane out of Boston at 11:25.

He got up early enough to find Bill Sears unlocking the gas pumps.

Since Bill heard about everything that happened in Elkhorn, he already knew that Quinn's cat had been killed. But when Michael asked, Bill said, "Haven't heard of anything else like that happening around here. Up north, yep. Not here, though."

Michael went on to Passamody. In his briefcase he carried a recorder, notes of some key questions to ask Pau Mai Hau. But he was thinking about Quinn. He stopped at the Passamody florist from which the box had come that had enclosed the April Fools' gift to Quinn. The clerk there looked at him as if he were out of his mind. For whom had she packed flowers in a box like that? How would she know? Dozens of people. Were there receipts? Sure. She got out receipts for the previous few days. Conscious of passing time, Michael flipped through them. The names meant nothing to him. None had an Elkhorn delivery address. The clerk claimed they were all regular customers. And besides, anybody could pick a box off a trash heap.

He gave up the forlorn hope and barely made his flight. He caught the Boston plane with only seconds to spare. On the trip to Baltimore he tried to work on his key questions. But he kept thinking of Quinn.

He landed, rented a car, and drove to Pikesville. Pau Mai Hau owned a restaurant now. He had once been the commandant of a prison in Vietnam. Michael had been there, seen the tiger cages, the deprivation, the despair. Combing the lists of boat people, the immigration records, for refugees who might interest him, he had come upon that familiar name.

Pau Mai Hau had agreed to the interview by phone. He was waiting. A small man, thin-faced when he had once been chubby, with sunken eyes that held no spark of laughter.

He greeted Michael, immediately asked how he had been traced. Michael explained, set up the recorder, began to ask his questions. The answers came hesitantly. Pau Mai Hau wanted to be an American. There could be no life for him in Vietnam. He'd hidden among the boat people, landed in Hong Kong. The money for the restaurant? He shrugged. He'd had savings. Gold. The prison? He shrugged again. A man did his job. And, irritably: What did the dead past matter? All that, the prison and its tiger cages, it was done.

Michael listened, thought of Quinn. The past was never done. She never spoke of it, of Washington. He asked further questions of Pau Mai Hau. But it was no good. He couldn't concentrate. Pikesville was too far from Quinn. Anything could happen.

He cut the interview short, asked permission to return another time.

When he reached Passamody, he called Helen. She told him that Quinn had gone that morning to Jewell's Landing on schedule.

He was in the coastal town in time to take her to dinner. When he asked her about her life in Washington, she turned his questions aside. They spent the night in the Landing Motel together. They didn't speak of the dead cat.

CHAPTER 15

A day later, Quinn was on Saugatuck Island.

Her fear had gone with her, the memory of Devil's staring eyes.

She did a day's work, changed her clothes and went down to the hotel dining room for an early dinner.

She was seated at a table for two between the draped windows. Behind her, the only other guests in the place also sat at a table for two.

They were middle-aged, and pleasant-looking. Though they spoke quietly, Quinn could hear their conversation.

"We could do the shopping tonight," Justin Belton suggested.

His wife Serena answered, "Tomorrow's soon enough."

"Then shall we have an after-dinner brandy?"

Serena smiled. "That would be nice."

Having finished their drinks, they rose to leave with friendly nods in Quinn's direction.

She had just had her dessert when a single man came in. He had longish chestnut hair, and wore metal-framed glasses. He sat in a distant corner. He took up the big menu, mumbling his order at the waiter.

From around the edge of the menu, Jerry watched Quinn. He knew everything about her. Passamody, Riverton, St. Mary's City, and Ballston. Jewell's Landing, and Saugatuck Island. He had learned Westbrook Road, and the dirt lane that led to the abandoned house on the hill. He hadn't even had to touch the black cat. A burlap bag and a pot of milk within it had trapped the wicked beast.

Jerry smiled down at the tablecloth. At first he'd been terribly afraid of the cat, but he needn't have been. The answer had come to him. It would all bloom in his mind, and he would know what to do. It was always that way.

His mouth was cottony now, his eyes afire. The slow sinewy muscles of her thighs, moving her away from him, the quick flash of her grin at the waiter. Jerry's vision blurred. He saw Jenny. His Jenny. She disappeared through the door into the hallway beyond.

The waiter put food before him. He ate sparingly.

Later he sat in the dark of the downstairs room, squeezing a pair of fur-lined tan suede gloves between his hands.

* * *

"Pretty girl," Justin Belton said, as he helped Serena into the car.

"Very," she agreed happily. There was nothing old about Justin, even if he was sixty-eight. She was pleased at the thought. She put her hand on his knee, and told him what she planned as the menu for the next evening's dinner party.

In the morning she readied herself to do the shopping. She tucked a gray curl under her hat, smoothed her scarf at the nape of her neck, and drew on her heavy woollen gloves. All the while she looked consideringly around the kitchen. "Have I everything I'll need?" she murmured.

Justin turned back to ask, "What did you say, Serena?"

"I'm talking to myself."

"Then talk louder so I can hear you." He grinned. "Is the list in your purse?"

"Oh, Justin! That's what I forgot." Again she studied the kitchen, this time with more clear intention. Still, in the back of her mind, she thought how much she enjoyed the new refrigerator, the gleaming stove, the built-in cabinets and counters, with dishwasher beneath.

She was glad she and Justin had done the remodeling. The house was old; she and Justin weren't young. The neighbors had thought them foolish. But she and Justin had talked it over, as they had every decision they had made in the thirty-four years of their marriage. They had reponsibility to no one but themselves. When Justin retired and sold his share of the shoe factory, and invested the proceeds, their income was enough to maintain them at the level to which they had long been accustomed. She liked entertaining. Therefore the new kitchen. It had been fun doing it together in spite of the quarrels with the contractors. She smiled at Justin.

"What now?" he asked. "You can't find it?"

"I forgot the list," she chuckled. "Admiring the results of our labors."

"If we're going before the store gets crowded . . ."

She pushed her gloved hand into her pocket. "I have it!"

She watched him put on his hat. Very dashing, she thought. And she liked his new mustache. As she passed him to go out, she raised herself on tiptoe and planted a warm kiss on his mouth.

It took only fifteen minutes to reach the shopping center. Serena went into Parkwood's, the list firmly clutched in her hand.

"We're low on gin," Justin told her. "While you're here I'll go next door and get half a gallon."

"You just want to do your bit of gambling. You can't fool me."

Forty-five minutes later, they had finished their shopping. He had loaded the car himself because the boy who usually helped him was busy.

Now he put the lottery ticket under the clip on the sun visor. It had become a habit to keep it there since he had been buying it. Once weekly he invested a dollar, laughing about it to himself. He didn't expect to win. Though a man could never tell. Not really. Mostly he did it because it amused Serena. It was worth a dollar to see her grin when he threw away the old ticket and put the new one up. It was worth it, too, to see how she watched his face when he checked the number in the newspaper every Thursday morning.

She caught his sidewise glance. "It doesn't matter if you win, Justin."

Laughing, he started on the short drive home. "Just exactly what I was thinking. And the last big killing I made was an aggie marble. It took me an hour and a half of manipulating the claw in one of those grab-bag machines they used to have back in the thirties. But I know that I'm lucky anyway."

At about the same time that Justin Belton parked before his house, Quinn reached the end of the Saugatuck Causeway, and turned south into the Coastal Road.

Jerry was one truck and two ski-laden cars behind her.

CHAPTER 16

It was steamy hot in the Turnpike Diner.

The early-morning fog that had hung over Riverton had receded before a faintly warming sun. But the heat was still on high, an acknowledgment that April's spring was more promise than reality.

The place was quiet except for the murmur of Shirley's voice answering the shoe factory guard who had come in for the usual three-coffees-and-doughnuts afternoon snack.

Jerry ignored the banter between those two. Without turning his head, he kept his eyes slanted through his steel-rimmed glasses to the place where Mary Baker sat alone at the end of the counter.

He had followed Quinn into Riverton the night before. He parked in an alley behind the Blue Bell Motel and watched her unload the Rabbit, her mink coat blowing around her legs, the tiny mink cap set firmly on her red-gold hair. Lucky Quinn Monroe, he'd thought. And then, Mary Baker was in his mind. Another lucky one. A pretty girl, with a husband, who was going to buy a *real* house.

Soon after, he parked his sedan at an angle in a spot near the trailer park. The next day, having trailed Quinn through Riverton, he was back.

Mary came out, walked down the road, head bent, shoulders sagging. He followed her to the Turnpike Diner . . .

There was a forced smile on her lips as she tried to hear the talk between Shirley and the factory guard. She pretended that she was part of the conversation, but she wasn't. Shirley and the guard ignored her and grinned only at each other.

Mary sagged on the stool. She had finished her coffee fifteen minutes ago, but Shirley hadn't noticed, so the mug was still empty.

Waiting patiently while Shirley laughed and swung her pageboy on her shoulders and the guard guffawed, Mary wondered why everything seemed so different to her now.

The money didn't seem real to her. It was in the bank where Gus wanted it. He'd said he'd decide pretty soon what they'd do. But she wasn't content with that. She wanted a proper house, one like Shirley's. She'd mentioned it to him a couple of times, but he just shrugged it off. More than that, though, she was waiting for things to be the way they had been before. She was wondering if they ever would.

There'd been those few days of excitement. The women in the trailer park had come in and laughed and congratulated her, and the men had been enviously teasing to Gus. Soon that stopped, though sometimes Molly Farran came by to see her. But nobody else did. She and Gus hadn't bought a new car or a real house. They hadn't gone away to Florida. They were stick-in-the-muds. Their neighbors lost interest.

With the return to normalcy, Mary noticed even more how peculiar it was between her and Gus. She felt that when she won the lottery she had done something that terribly displeased him. It didn't make sense. But that's how it was.

"See you, Shirley," the guard was saying.

"Same time, same place," she grinned as he went out. She refilled the mug in front of a man wearing glasses, then came swinging down the counter. "That boy's still in there trying. Him and his phony uniform and phony brass buttons."

"How come you don't go out with him?"

"I've got better fish to fry," Shirley answered. She poured coffee for Mary, leaned an elbow on the counter. "What's the matter? You look down and out."

"Nothing."

"Nothing!" Shirley's black eyes snapped. "I'll bet it's nothing. What's Gus done?"

Mary sipped coffee. It was hot enough to burn her lips. She set the mug down, blew out. "Oh, boy."

Shirley ignored the attempted diversion. "I've been thinking about it, and I still don't understand. How come you handed all that dough over to Gus? How come you didn't keep it for yourself?"

"I didn't want to," Mary answered, as if that explained everything. And: "It belongs to us both."

"*You* won it," Shirley retorted.

"What difference does that make?"

"Come on," Shirley said. "No kidding now. What *are* you going to do with the dough?"

"I don't know. Maybe we just won't do anything."

"And what about the house?"

"I don't know yet, Shirley." Mary wished now that she'd kept her mouth shut. In the excitement of the win, she's said what she wanted most. To Shirley. To the man from the Lottery Commission, too. So everybody knew.

"Waiting for Gus to make up his mind?" Shirley said.

"I guess so."

"You're crazy. That's what's wrong with you. Oh, if it was me—if only I'd won—boy, what a time I'd have. I'd get me a new car, something small and easy to handle, and Riverton would see the last of me. I'd go down to Boston, and load up with a batch of new clothes." She stopped, sighed. "You're just plain crazy, Mary Baker."

Later, Shirley used the same word. She lay in bed with Gus. Through the window, she could see a rectangle of black sky, the white and red landing lights of a plane coming in. She turned to snuggle against him, to run a finger through the coppery hair on his chest. "Crazy. That's what it is, Gus. You just letting it sit in the bank."

"I'm thinking," he told her gruffly.

"You think too much."

"Maybe."

"And what're you thinking about?"

He didn't answer. The first time Mary had asked her to dinner, she came, bringing a bottle of wine. She flashed that knowing grin at him, and turning away, she swung that saucy ass at him, and all of a sudden, he had a bone between his legs he could hardly believe. She was a goddamn interfering broad you couldn't trust as far as you could spit, and he wanted her.

"It's Mary," Shirley said.

"Something like that."

"Just what I told you. You think too much."

"And you talk too much." He pushed her away, sat up.

"If you say so, I'll stop talking. Only one of these days you're going to tell me what we're going to do about her."

"Nothing," he said harshly. "You keep your mouth shut and I'll keep mine shut."

Her black eyes narrowed. Her lush mouth thinned. She said, "I can do that. But I wonder about you."

He put a hand on her breast, forefinger and thumb rolling the nipple. "Forget it." He spoke to himself as well as to her. *Forget it. Forget Mary.* He'd given her everything she wanted. He'd taken care of her for years. This had nothing to do with her. It was Shirley time.

And Shirley said softly, "You think you can have it all, don't you?"

He didn't answer. He rolled over, so that his body covered hers, and inched her thighs open, and sank himself into her so that he wouldn't have to think anymore.

It was late. He came in beer-flushed, silent. He cast a look at the pie on the table, the perking coffee on the stove.

"Want anything?" Mary asked brightly.

"I'll be out in a minute." He escaped into the bathroom. Her dark blue eyes, big, questioning . . . her mouth curled in a forced smile . . . the fake brightness in her voice . . . He showered away the smell of Shirley, the velvet feel of her hot body. Damn her to hell!

When he sat at the table in the galley, Mary asked, "Big day?"

"So-so."

"It'll get easier soon."

"Backhoes and mowers instead of snowplows."

"Better weather always makes for better days. And I can feel them both coming."

"Sure." He drank the coffee she served him, ate the slice of pie.

"Gus . . ." she said tentatively. Then, in a rush: "Gus, listen, what's the matter?"

He grunted, pushed his bulk up. "I'm tired. I'm going to bed."

Later, lying beside him, conscious of the vast distance between them although they were only inches apart, she said into the darkness, "Have you been thinking about the house, Gus?"

"Not much. What do we need it for? We're comfortable here."

"But I'd like a house," she said gently.

"Forget it, Mary," Gus answered, and remembered saying the same thing to Shirley only a little while ago.

In the morning, he told Mary that he might stop for a couple of beers with the boys, and might not. She told him she'd have dinner ready, just in case.

He spent the first half of the day in the yards, telling himself that he'd go straight home after work. He spent the second half of the day aware of a growing ache in his groin. He cut his hand on a piece of wire, licked off the blood and grease, and kept on working until the foreman shoved a first-aid kit under his nose. The lunch Mary had fixed for him lay like a rock in his gut.

At four thirty, when he quit, he had his two beers in Henley's. He started to go home. The pickup went to Engleton Road and Shirley's.

"I went to the movies with him," Shirley said, grinning. "And he's not so bad as I thought. At least he only wanted to hold hands, and that's a new wrinkle."

Mary listened, sipped her coffee. The shoe factory guard had just left. He and Shirley had been laughing together for fifteen minutes. Mary had supposed that something had happened.

Shirley went on, "And tonight we're going to go dancing. I guess that's when the struggle'll begin."

"Maybe he's just a nice guy that wants to get to know you better."

"That's what I mean. He wants to get to know me better."

Mary grinned. "Just what I said."

"Innocent," Shirley sighed. "When're you going to learn? They're all alike, and only after one thing."

"Maybe."

"Not maybe. Yes. And even your Gus, too," Shirley told her.

Mary set down her coffee mug. The stool beneath her seemed to swing and swoop. Shirley's black eyes were bottomless pits, and Mary felt that if she didn't cling hard to the counter she might fall into them, drown in them. There was something, something . . . She didn't want to know. She whispered hoarsely, "Remember that day we went to the Greentree? We ought to do that again sometime."

Shirley let her breath out. "Sure," she said carelessly. "Why not? One of these days. And maybe I'll even treat."

It was the same night. Gus found Shirley's cottage dark again. He sat in the truck and waited. He was there when she came home. He knew she saw the truck and recognized it. He watched as she swung up the walk, followed by a tall thin young man. Gus watched as their two separate shadows became one. He saw the door open, the shadows separate to go inside, the lights go on. He was still there when the tall young man emerged, whistling softly, and drove away.

Gus went to the door. He knocked gently, whistled.

Soon Shirley was there, grinning up at him.

He shoved her aside, and went in.

She closed the door, leaned against it, her blouse pulled out of her skirt, her pageboy in disarray, the dark lipstick smeared so that her lips were more lush-looking than ever.

"I thought you'd have sense enough to go home," she said.

"I don't want you fooling around."

"That doesn't count, Gus."

"I don't want you fooling around," he repeated. He put both hands palm flat on the door, his arms a cage that enclosed her.

She stared at him silently, then thrust herself at him, the full weight of her full body shoving at him. "Go home to your Mary, Gus."

He braced against her, jowls reddening. "You asked for it," he said thickly. "All the time, through her, you kept asking for it. Sending her to me with her 'Shirley said.' You were after me before I ever even saw you."

She laughed into his face. "You think so, hunh? You think you're the only man in the world?"

He slapped her twice, hard. Her head rocked back and she staggered, but her hands clawed, reaching for his eyes.

He caught her up and carried her through the hall into the lower-floor bedroom, and they tore at each other's clothes just as they had done the first time they had been together.

Afterward, when they lay panting side by side, she said coolly, "Okay, Gus. That was pretty nice. But I'm finished with you. Don't come back here anymore."

Mary looked at the wall clock for the hundredth time. The illuminated dial said twelve thirty. Later than usual for Gus. Outside the dogs yowled. She peered from the window. The trailer park was black as pitch. The road empty. She closed the jet under the coffeepot, covered the pie with a napkin, and went to bed.

She squeezed her eyes tightly shut and curled on her side and pretended to be asleep when Gus finally came in. But she was thinking about the time Gus made her quit the job with Becker's before she even started, and tall redheaded Quinn Monroe, who seemed to know how to do everything on her own.

Mary was up before the alarm as usual and fixed his lunch, filling the box with his favorite foods. His breakfast was ready and on the table when he came into the galley, yawning behind his hand.

She saw that he wouldn't quite look at her. His eyes were on his eggs, on the stove, at the window. She knew that Shirley was right. Gus was like the rest of them after all. But still, he was all she had. She had to try. She said, "I was thinking about the money again,

Gus. We ought to buy the house with it. It's the best investment there is for you and me, isn't it?"

"I don't want to talk about it now."

"Now's as good a time as any."

"Who says?"

"Me," she said quietly. "I say so. I really do want a house, Gus. I won that money. Not you. Me. I ought to have some say in what we do with it. We don't have to live in a trailer anymore, and I don't want to."

"You were always satisfied with it before."

"I'm not now."

He gave her a long hard stare. He didn't look when she thrust a list of houses they could see under his nose. She wasn't the Mary he'd married and loved. She'd turned into somebody else on him. Finally he said, "Nag, nag, nag, I don't know what's happening to us. All you can do is talk about a real house, like Shirley's. And pushing at me, pushing all the time. Even telling that Lottery Commission publicity guy so it'd be on the radio and in the papers. You and your real house!"

"I just want you to think about it, Gus."

He didn't answer. He finished his breakfast quickly, got his coat. "See you."

She just looked at him.

Ashamed, he came back from the door, and bent his head. His lips landed somewhere between her mouth and her ear. She touched the thinning brushed-forward hair on his head, but he pulled away. "Later, Mary."

When he was gone, she moved slowly through her morning chores. By noon she was at the Turnpike Diner.

Shirley was busy, tossed a brief "Hi, Mary," her way when pouring the coffee. After the rush, she came and told Mary about her second date with the shoe factory guard, shrugging, "I guess he'll do for a while. Until somebody better comes along."

Mary didn't ask about the powdered-over bruise high on Shirley's cheekbone, didn't encourage the talk about the factory guard. Shirley went off to serve a trucker at the end of the counter.

Mary left money for her coffee. She buttoned her coat. Outside, on the road, she stopped to listen to the rumble of the passing trucks on the All-State, then she began the walk home.

The still bare trees were blurred. The sunlight dimmed. The moving traffic muted. She couldn't look. She walked with her head down, focused on her own footsteps. One foot before the other. One scuffed toe. The other scuffed toe. The quick steps beat out a rhythm that cut the distance into small parts. Then the rhythm broke. Fear overwhelmed her. She ran.

Panting, the air burning in her throat, she raced to the trailer park. The familiar yowls greeted her, but this time she ignored them. Let the dogs come. She didn't care. They didn't come.

She flung open the door to her home, and looked, and fell sagging against the wall.

From where she stood she could see into the narrow closet, the bare hangers. She knew that Gus was gone.

The sun crept across the floor. It turned a dust ball into a half-melted golden nugget. It streaked the scuffed toe of Mary's right shoe. She looked at the dust and streak, and realized that she had seen them just so before. Once. Twice.

From the damp and sweaty chair in which she was sprawled, she could see the gas range, the small oven beneath.

Now she dragged her eyes away. She had studied both for two whole days, readying herself. She knew it would be easy.

There had been April rain to accompany her tears. She and Gus wouldn't sit in the summer sun under the roof he had built. She wouldn't hang his work pants and shirts on the lines he had strung in the back.

She got up from the chair, stiff, sore, hurting like the one time she had been belt-whipped in the orphanage for something she hadn't done. She took off her wrinkled coat. As she put it into the closet empty of Gus's clothes, she saw that something lay under the sugar bowl, centered on the galley table. She went past the oven without looking at it. She didn't have to. It was settled. The something under the sugar bowl was money. Three twenty-dollar bills. She swallowed convulsively, thinking of the Greentree, and Shirley, and a day when they had laughed together and stopped to buy lottery tickets in a variety store.

Next to the money she saw a green bank book. When she picked it up, it fell open to the middle, the last transaction. BALANCE . . . 00,000.00.

She felt neither regret nor surprise. It didn't matter that Gus had taken the money when he left. What did she want with it when she didn't have him?

She went into the bathroom. It was important that she be clean.

She spent an hour under the hot spray, not realizing how much time had passed. When she stepped out into the chill of the bathroom, she stubbed her toe on the commode. She had done it a thousand times before, and each time wished that Gus would want to live in a proper house, like Shirley's. He hadn't wanted to. Even with the money, when they could have, he still didn't want to.

Powdered, perfumed, hair brushed and gleaming, she carefully chose her skirt and blouse, and clipped on the earrings Gus had given her for Christmas two years before.

She ached. A gnawing worked at her. She made a sandwich of peanut butter and swallowed it. She drank a tall glass of milk. Having cleared away, swept the floor, done everything she could think of doing, she decided it was time.

Everything she had ever wanted was gone.

What was there left?

She was ending as she'd begun. Alone.

Tearless, unafraid, she looked at the oven. She saw it all in dark detail. Her head cushioned on the open door. Her body at full length on the linoleum. The lipstick on her mouth, mascara on her lashes. Fresh polish on her pumps. Sometime she'd go from sleep to that other thing.

Except . . . except . . . She didn't believe it. It wasn't true. It couldn't happen.

She turned from the oven. The walls were too close. She needed air. She grabbed her coat from the closet and hurried out.

Habit took her to the Turnpike Diner.

Shirley said, "I was wondering about you. Haven't seen you for a couple of days. You okay?"

Mary nodded, unable to speak.

"You look funny."

"It's Gus," Mary whispered. "He's gone."

Shirley leaned closer, her bottomless black eyes staring into Mary's. "And he took the money with him, didn't he?"

"Everything. Clothes. Pickup. Everything. He's gone."

"So what did I tell you? You should have listened. He's just like the rest of them."

Mary didn't answer, but she heard the hatred in Shirley's voice. Hatred.

Shirley's hand curled gently around Mary's cheek, fingers stroking, smoothing. "Men! All the same. What do you need them for anyhow? You'll get along, a pretty little thing like you. You'll get along okay."

Something in Shirley was reaching for Mary. She sensed it, knew it was there. An invisible current sucked at her while Shirley's eyes stared into hers. The hand at her cheek was silky, but it was like Gus's hand. The black eyes blazed with a look that had once blazed in Gus's eyes.

Mary understood. Shirley had always hated Gus because she wanted Mary for herself. Jealousy made her talk Gus down.

Mary caught up her coat and fled.

Hours and miles later, she stopped in front of the Blue Bell Motel. She remembered the day Shirley had driven her there and parked and told her about Quinn Monroe and Becker's. She'd never see Shirley again. Never talk to her, never look into those blazing black eyes. She remembered when Gus had sat in his pickup while she returned the sample case and apologized for changing her mind. It was Gus who'd changed her mind. But he was gone, too. Maybe someday she'd hear from him. She guessed it would be through divorce papers. He'd want another woman, a wife he could push around. She'd sign his papers. She and Gus were done.

She knew it was Monday without thinking about it, just as she had decided where she was going when she fled the Turnpike Diner without thinking about it.

She went into the foyer and asked the desk clerk for Quinn Monroe. He said Miss Monroe was expected, but hadn't yet checked in. She ought to arrive within a few hours, and when she did, he'd be glad to pass along any message.

Mary pondered, then wrote a few words. "I'd like to see you. I'll come back at five." She signed it, "Mary Easter."

Mary Easter, she said to herself as she went out. That's my name. That's me. I'm Mary Easter.

She walked quickly down the block. She was hungry. No. Starving. She passed the bank where Gus had put her winnings into his account. She went to the People's Fair and sat at the counter, where they had had coffee together that day. She remembered, but she was still starving. She ordered a club sandwich, and a milkshake, and sat back, sighing with relief. She had made it that far. She could keep on going.

It was dark but a single light burned in the trailer.

Jerry stared at it balefully. What was wrong with her? She was pretty, young, rich. She was alive. Lucky. But she hadn't done a thing. If only it had been Jenny. But Jenny was dead. And Mary Baker was alive.

He sat listening to his transistor for hours. Nothing came to him. His hands squeezed together, as if he had her by the throat. But it didn't flower. It didn't bloom in him. He didn't see what to do, or how. So he told himself to wait. It would come to him. At dawn he was back at the Blue Bell Motel, ready for Quinn to come out.

CHAPTER 17

Jerry first heard about it on an early-morning newscast.

Adelaide Herman, of St. Mary's City, wife of George Herman, a local building contractor, had just won seventy thousand dollars in the lottery.

Another lucky one. Lucky and alive, Jerry thought. The name sank slowly into his mind. As he glanced into his rearview mirror, he saw the glow of Quinn's hair in the May sun, her head over the Rabbit's steering wheel. He forgot Adelaide Herman.

George Herman first heard about it three days after it actually happened. It was a Monday afternoon. Along with a number of other St. Mary's City businessmen, he was in the bar of the club. He stood hunched over the mahogany counter. He was the only one who had been there continuously since the place opened at eleven o'clock. He knew he was drunk and getting drunker. He didn't care.

"Let me have another," he growled. And, as the bartender added water to the whiskey: "Straight, for Christ's sake! How many times do I have to tell you?"

The man poured a fresh drink, looking sidewise at the cluster of members nearby.

George accepted the glass put before him, frowned into it, and emptied it in two long swallows. It wasn't helping. Nothing would. Not this nightmare morning. He'd gone to the development to give it one last look. A farewell to his hopes and dreams. His creditors had come on him like vultures. Soon he'd have to go home and tell Adelaide, and see the contempt in her eyes.

"Hey, George! Congratulations!" It was Ben Blakely, who drank only white wine cut with Perrier water, who had never made a wrong move in his life and was worth half a million to prove it. "How does it feel to be a winner, George?"

George swung his head sideways. "What the hell are you talking about?"

"The lottery. Didn't you know?"

"What lottery?"

Ben Blakely grinned. "I guess you don't know what your Adelaide's done."

"Adelaide?"

"Your wife, George."

"What about her?"

"She's just picked up seventy thousand dollars."

George was very still. From toes to eyeballs he felt paralyzed. Turned to ice. At last, throat melting slightly, he gasped, "It must be a mistake."

"Her name was on the list last Friday. Mrs. Adelaide Herman, Belair. Seventy thousand dollars."

"Friday," George muttered.

"I figured you did all your gambling in construction. How's the development doing, anyway?"

"Good," George said. Old habit doing his talking for him. Cover the trouble. Maybe it'll go away. Admit to nothing and maybe nothing won't happen.

"I'm glad to hear that. There were rumors."

"Rumors," George shrugged.

The feeling was coming back to him now. He could count his heartbeats against his ribs. He could breathe. Seventy thousand dollars less the seller's commission, whatever it was, less the income tax, whatever that was.

The leavings would still be enough to save him. To give him space and time. Bless Adelaide.

He gestured at the bartender for the chit and signed with a flourish.

He hurried out to his car, started in a quick tire-spinning rush for Belair. Halfway there, he eased the pressure on the accelerator. How come she hadn't told him? He decided it was going to be a surprise. She was waiting for the check. When she received it, or collected it, however it was done, she would present it to him. He would pay off the heaviest of his creditors. He'd have a chance. Nothing was going to be lost.

On the crest of that optimism, he let himself into the house, yelled, "Adelaide? You here?"

"Upstairs," she called back. Then: "Coming."

She appeared on the landing. She was the same as always, every blond hair in place, a ruffle of white at her throat, pearls looped beneath it.

He grinned as she came toward him. "You're really something, you know it?"

"What?" Perplexed. Faintly frowning. When she reached the foyer, she went on. "Is something wrong, George?"

He stared at her, suddenly unsure. Maybe there was another Adelaide Herman. Maybe Ben Blakely had made a mistake. Or pulled some crazy practical joke. I'll kill him, George thought. I'll wring his rich neck for him.

"George?"

Either there was something wrong or she ought to be in the movies. She was the best actress in the world.

He said, "Listen, quit playing games. It's too important. Did it really happen?"

Understanding dawned on her face. She sighed. She walked past him into the living room. Her shoulders were very straight, the full skirt swinging around her. She stopped in front of the fireplace, her head at the mantel just below the two guns centered in brackets on the wall. "I gather that you've heard."

Relief wilted him. He said, "You don't know what it means. It'll save us, Adelaide. Seventy thousand dollars . . ." He was grinning. He started toward her, his arms out to hug her.

"No, George," she said quietly.

It was like a blow exploding from nowhere into his solar plexus. It stopped him in midstep. Mouth ajar, he stared at her, certain that he had heard her rightly, certain that he understood, but filled with disbelief.

"No," she repeated softly. "My winnings are mine, and you're not going to throw good money after bad."

"But I need—"

"Sorry." And she was. But just a little. Not nearly enough to change her mind.

"Adelaide, you don't really mean— We're married, for God's sake. Don't you remember—for better or worse, and when we—"

She cut in. "I remember everything."

"You'll ruin me. You'll ruin us. You have as much to lose as I have."

"But *I'll* have just about seventy thousand dollars."

"To throw away on Evan," George yelled.

"I'll do whatever I want to with it, and you can't stop me!"

George went to the cabinet, took out a bottle of scotch and poured a tall whiskey. He drank it down. His face was flushed at the cheeks but gray around his jaws and eyes. Finally, he said, "You don't trust me with your money, is that it?"

"I don't trust you with anything."

"What the hell does that mean?"

"Figure it out, George."

"I can't. I don't understand. All I know is I thought a miracle had happened to save us. And now it's as if I've gone crazy. A miracle happened okay. But only for you."

"That's quite right," she said softly. "It's the first time you've been right in many long years." As she went on her voice grew louder, more shrill. "Why should I trust you? What should I trust you with? My hopes, my dreams, my body, my love?"

"I'm your husband. Of course you trust me."

"But I don't! And you know it! And you know why! I don't have reason to. How could I? You and your tarts. Did you think I didn't know about them? Did you think you were hiding them from me? Or did you ever think at all, except with that thing you carry between your legs?"

"My tarts?" he repeated, eyes blank, jaw unslung.

"The first one when I was carrying Evan. Your secretary—so called. What was her name? Well, never mind. I saw the two of you. With my own eyes. And it broke my heart. It finished me forever, George. It was your fault."

"Oh, my God," he cried. "A man gets hungry for it. So what? I fired her afterward, didn't I? So what were you burning about?"

"I saw you. It made me sick forever."

"Made you sick? You never seemed sick to me. You had everything you ever wanted. Mink coats, diamond rings . . . this house. You even had Evan more than I ever did."

"And the others," she went on, ignoring George. "All your other little popsies over the years—"

"What did you expect when all I ever got was cold tail at home? What was I supposed to do? Get on my knees and beg for it?"

"You could have tried."

"And you'd have laughed. Because you always knew those girls didn't mean a thing to me. What did they take from you? You stayed my wife, Adelaide."

"I didn't know any better until it was too late."

"Those girls had nothing to do with you."

"They had too much to do with me, George. You wrecked me

with your little flings. Each one made me feel a little bit less than a woman, less than a person even. Each one made me think I wasn't worth anything to you, to any man. All I had left was Evan. But now I have the money." There was a high flush of triumph on her cheeks, and her eyes glittered with it. "The money, George."

"You're crazy," he cried. He stood swaying, blinking, looking into Adelaide's suddenly unfamiliar face. "But whatever, you've got to help me. I can't lose everything."

"No, George, I'm sorry, but the answer is no. Go to your tarts for what you need. Don't ask me to help you. Not anymore. I'm going to see Evan through college. I'm going to take care of myself. I'm not going to throw my winnings away on you."

He started for her, hands out in a gesture that was half pleading, half threatening. "I don't believe you. You can't do it."

She stood her ground, fingers curled in the pearls at her throat.

"Listen," he cried. "Listen! I beg you. I'm begging you, Adelaide. Not for me. But for us. Save Hermad. For us."

"Damn Hermad!" she shrilled. "And damn you with it."

"I won't let—you can't—"

He closed the space between them, moving slowly, a man struggling against a compelling current.

The stone of the fireplace was at her shoulders. She felt their chill. She said softly, "Stop it, George."

His hands fell on her shoulders, jerked her closer. The strands of pearls at her throat broke. Gleaming beads fell in a soundless random dance to the thick carpet.

"Stop it," she repeated hoarsely.

"You've got to give me that money," he snarled, his eyes blank and blind. When she turned her face away, he hit her. He hit her again as she fell against the cold stone at her back, and then again as she brought her arms up between them.

Her vision blurred. She tasted blood in her mouth, and spat the chip of a tooth at him.

His hand went back one more time. She grabbed a gun from the rack over the mantel and brought it down. Its muzzle raked a long bleeding furrow along George's cheek as it swung in a wide arc.

He roared a curse, grappling for it.

"No," she screamed. "No. No."

Her fingers jerked. A sudden deafening blast.

George stumbled and fell, blank surprise smoothing the rage from his face. A raw gout of blood leaped from his chest.

Still screaming, Adelaide covered her eyes and ran from the house.

In a little while sirens shrilled their way into the quiet lanes of Belair.

CHAPTER 18

Bobsie made his "mama" sound, and Dorsey picked him up, hugged him. "There's my good boy. There's my sweetie."

Carrie said, "We've had a good deal. This weather's always easier."

"Isn't it?" Dorsey tried to keep the jubilation from her voice, her face. She didn't want anybody to know. Not even Carrie.

It had taken a long time. But today, at precisely three o'clock, she had figured out the second step. The first step was easy. Chances were better in the bonus game. They would only play that one. She had casually told Carrie to switch her buys. The second step came harder.

But Ethel Johnson had sneezed, and Dorsey saw the whole thing in her mind.

She knew exactly how she would manage it. When the time came. That is, when the right number was in the bonus game. Now she asked, "Get the ticket, Carrie?"

"You bet I did." Carrie sighed. "But maybe we're just crazy."

"Oh, I don't think so. I've just got a feeling . . . one of these days."

Carrie laughed. "It doesn't hurt to dream, I guess."

Bobsie made his "cake" sound, and Carrie asked, "Want some? It's all ready, and coffee, too."

But Dorsey was afraid she couldn't keep her mouth shut if she stayed. She wanted it to be a real surprise to Carrie. She wanted nobody to know, nobody, except herself, how she managed what was supposedly absolutely impossible. She said, "I guess not. I've got a load of laundry to do you wouldn't believe."

A few minutes later, hugging Bobsie to her, she left for home, the most excited woman that evening in St. Mary's City.

A dusty tan sedan was parked a block from the Herman house when Adelaide, flanked by her son Evan, and her lawyer, left for the Center Street police station.

It trailed them there unnoticed, then parked, when the three went in. By the time they came out, it was gone.

That night, as he lay in his bed in the Capitol Hotel, Jerry listened to the radio and brooded on Adelaide Herman, who was rich and beautiful and lucky and had everything. And who was pleading self-defense in the murder of her husband. Nothing came to him, although he kept asking himself what right she had to be ALIVE. Soon he wept, telling himself that it wasn't right. None of it was. Not when his Jenny had died. But when he fell asleep it was to dream of Quinn Monroe.

It was a floor below, and morning.

Quinn watched as Michael slid his tie knot under his collar, hunching forward to see himself in the mirror.

A little while ago they had been as close as a man and woman could be. Now they were separate again. It was as if there had been no moments when their two needs were joined while they themselves, in flesh, were joined. Soon he would go one way, she another. One would then be two. She knew he would think of her; she would think of him. Those thoughts would be the only connection between them. Still, they wouldn't really be two. The bond was there. He had said he would change her. He had.

She was suddenly breathless with unnamable fright. She sat up abruptly, folding her legs under her. A strap of her green gown slipped low on one shoulder. Her hair, flowing loose, was touched with the morning sun of May.

He saw her first in the mirror, then turned to look at her directly. "What's the matter, Quinn?"

"Nothing." Her voice was composed, giving away no clue to her fear, but he felt into it, sensed it.

He watched her, saw her fingers pluck aimlessly at the blanket, tearing away pink fluff. "Something happen?"

She shook her head. "I ought to get started, is all."

"I'll be out of your way in a minute."

"It's okay. I'm not in that much of a hurry."

"You're going on to Ballston this afternoon?"

"Yes," she answered.

He decided on the spur of the moment. "I'll have to spend a few hours at the Capitol. How about lunch with me before you leave?"

"Good."

He bent to kiss her. "Quinn . . ."

She glanced at her watch. "Michael, I *do* have to get started."

He went to the door, grinned at her. "I know, the ladies of St.

Mary's City await you." But he hesitated, hand on the knob. Then he turned back to her. "Listen, Quinn, I have to talk to you."

"At lunch," she said.

"Now." He returned to the bed, sat beside her. "I've been thinking about it for a couple of weeks, but I wanted to wait and see how it went. Now I'm sure. I won't be able to get the book done in time. And I have to finish it before I leave, so I want you to delay until September."

"The reservations, Michael—you know I've begun making them."

"They can be changed. I'll do it myself." He drew a deep breath, grinned, and took both her hands. "I hadn't quite finished what I wanted to say. Wait until September, and we'll make your trip our honeymoon."

Her eyes widened. For an instant she saw them riding across a moonlit desert on swaying camels, the Sphinx in the distance. Then she was alone, the empty desert black with shadow. She saw a long way down a narrow road, the two of them together. Then she saw herself bereft again. "No," she whispered painfully. "No, Michael, I'm sorry. I—I just can't—"

"No to which of the two proposals?" he demanded, feeling the chill in her hands.

"I don't want to delay until September, Michael."

"And . . . ?"

She drew a deep breath, pulled her hands from his. It had been easier to say no to Lew Selby. To say it to Michael was purest pain. But she had to. She moved numb lips to tell him, "I guess I just don't want to marry. I like things the way they are."

"And that's enough for you?"

She nodded.

He got to his feet. "I told you I'm bullheaded. We'll talk about it more over lunch."

But by then, everything had changed.

The outside damp followed Quinn into the hotel lobby. She was looking forward to a quick shower before she met Michael.

She was firmly resolved to avoid any further discussion of marriage. She had what she wanted. It was enough. She would go on her trip as she had always dreamed. The treasure-laden ship that Jenny had once mentioned to her had actually sailed in when Quinn's lottery number came up. She would see the mountain fortresses of

Kabul, and explore its crowded bazaars. She'd have no ties, be free to meet adventure, even romance, when it came. It couldn't be the same if she had a husband. Leaving Michael would be hard. But she would do it. She had to be true to her dream. She convinced herself that weakness was the danger. But she was going to be strong. She knew enough about hurt. So she'd make herself say goodbye to Michael when the time came.

The debate had been tiring, she told herself, as she went to the desk for her room key; the weather had been warm; she'd been overdressed. That was why she felt so drained.

The clerk wasn't behind the desk. She supposed he was off attending to some chore.

She took her key from the box and went up the steps and started down the long still corridor to her room. A breeze blew in her face. A door at the far end, her door, suddenly jerked open, then slammed shut with a reverberating bang.

She remembered clearly that she had locked it carefully when she had left earlier. The key had stuck. She'd had to jiggle it to make it work, and she'd been certain to try the knob before turning away, her head still achurn with Michael's proposal.

Now, with the bang of the slamming door still echoing in her ears, she ran the rest of the short distance down the hall. But at the threshold of the room, she stopped, gently eased the door open, and looked in.

The window had been raised to the fullest. Gray curtains flapped inside on gusts of gray mists, the May sun of morning gone.

Quinn's order book and purse fell from her nerveless hands. Cosmetics rolled at her feet. Paper drifted away to dark corners as she made a slow shivering survey of the place.

The room was empty now, but someone had been there.

Shreds of fabric floated around her ankles.

The closet door was ajar.

Cautiously she went to it.

The garment bag in which she had packed her clothes for the week's travels lay on the floor. She knew it by its color, but it had no shape and no form. It had been ripped into long streamers.

Nothing of what she had brought with her remained intact. The white sweater was a pile of crinkled woollen ravelings. The blue skirt was in ribbons. The green gown was in tatters. She supposed the red blouse was somewhere in the debris, but she couldn't see it.

Wide-eyed, gasping, she backed from the closet, then the room.

At the end of the corridor there were muffled footsteps. A tall looming shadow.

She wavered indecisively, swaying first one way, then the other. She wanted to run, but she couldn't. Her body refused to obey her. Her mind admitted that there was no place to go.

The threatening shadow resolved itself into Michael's familiar form.

Dizzy with relief, she cried his name.

His long loping stride became a lunge. Reaching to enfold her in his arms, he demanded, "What's wrong?"

"Someone—something—"

Still holding her, he pushed open the door to the room, took a single look. Then he put her aside, went in. He got her purse, a few of the things that had fallen from it, and returned to her.

His throat was dry. A pulse hammered behind his eyes, the impulse that had guided the knife frightened him. He said only, "Let's go see the clerk."

The man was back at his desk. He listened, frowned. Then: "I don't see how it could've happened. But I had things to do. A big party checked in. Seven. And they needed help with their bags. We're a city hotel, after all. Anybody can walk in." He spread his hands. "So—"

When Michael spoke of the police, the clerk frowned even more deeply. "All right. Sure. I'll call. If you want. But what good will it do?"

"Call," Michael said abruptly.

As the man went to the telephone, there was a staccato of heels on the steps. A small plump young woman raced to the desk, gasping, "Somebody's been in my room!" She flung what seemed to be a bundle of rags at him. "My skirt and blouse are ruined!"

"You, too?" Quinn said softly. "We've just called the police." She was nearly weak with relief. If this woman's clothing had also been despoiled, then what had happened could not have been an attack on her. It had to be a coincidence. It couldn't have anything to do with her lottery win.

By the time the clerk had completed his call, there was another complaint of torn clothing. A tall thin woman, with lavender hair set in tiny waves, indignantly displayed what was left of her favorite two-piece outfit.

The constable arrived, listened. Then: "All three of you?" he said when he heard. "Right at the end of the corridor, and next door to each other?" He took off his cap, scratched his head, and replaced his cap with careful deliberation. "I don't know. It's a funny damn thing, isn't it?"

"The hotel is not responsible," the clerk said.

Michael scowled at him, but spoke to the constable. "What can you do?"

"I'd better go see. That's the first thing." The constable ambled slowly across the foyer to the steps and climbed them. When he returned ten minutes later, he said, "Looks like you had some wild kids running through. They got into those rooms and had their fun. Laughing now. Miles away."

"And . . . ?" Michael asked.

"It'll go on the books. We'll pick them up one of these times," the constable answered.

The hotel coffee shop. Tables empty but uncleared after the midday rush.

Michael looked at Quinn. He had spent the major part of the morning marshaling his arguments. He had determined to convince her to delay until September, and make the trip their honeymoon. He wasn't going to give her up, and that was that.

But now everything had changed.

He said soberly, "This is more of the same, Quinn. Only worse."

She nodded, visibly braced. The nightmare had begun with a newscast, Helen's question about Jenny Lakas, and an empty bottle of wine. Those seemingly inconsequential moments had led to the meeting with Michael, the lottery ticket, and the letters.

Michael was saying, "For a couple of minutes I tried to believe that it was a coincidence. It wasn't."

"I tried to think the same." Her voice was a dry whisper. Suddenly there were dark thumbprints under her eyes. "But kids wouldn't have destroyed everything of mine, and so little belonging to those other women."

"Which is why we have to talk, Quinn."

She hadn't heard directly from *A Friend* since he'd written to her from Passamody months before. But she knew his presence. He made himself known, spoke to her wordlessly. He came closer each time. A hovering disaster that awaited her.

Swift, sudden panic overwhelmed her. She jumped to her feet, fled toward the door. Run, run. He was somewhere still near.

Michael went after her, caught her by the shoulders and spun her into his arms to hold her tightly.

But by the time he had reached her, she had already stopped. Why was she running? What good would it do? Where was she going?

Gently, he wiped the cold sweat from her brow. Then: "Come on. We'll have some coffee." He led her back to the table.

When they'd been served, he said, "I'm going to put a stop to this business. But you're going to have to help me." He waited. She didn't answer. "Quinn, listen, you must have some idea. Some clue to whoever first wrote to you."

"The letters just came. The rest followed." She swallowed hard. No use to run.

"One of your girls maybe? Somebody who thinks she has a grudge against you, or maybe against Becker's?"

"They're all my friends," Quinn protested.

"On the outside maybe, but sometimes, underneath, there's a festering dislike—a jealousy—"

"I don't know anybody who's been to Kansas City."

"You can't be certain of that."

"I can't be certain of anything anymore. Except that it all goes back to the lottery win and the letters. And that they began in Kansas City, and whoever wrote them has come to Passamody and Elkhorn."

"Helen?" Michael asked. "I know you're fond of her. But think a minute. She's middle-aged, lonely, unhappy. Sometimes—"

Quinn shook her head. "It's impossible. And if you don't believe me, then call Helen in Elkhorn right now. If she'd been here in St. Mary's City, she couldn't have gotten home yet."

He rose, fishing for change in his pocket.

She watched him disappear into the lobby, a vise tightening around her heart. She imagined herself saying, "Yes, Michael. Let's go together in September." An instant of sweet hope flooded her. She fought it down with an effort that made her tremble. Sometime, somehow, she would fail him. The way she had failed Jenny.

"You're right about Helen," he said, returning. "She's home." Then: "But what about in your traveling around? Have you ever seen anyone that looked familiar? I mean, somebody that you think you've maybe seen before?"

She considered, then shook her head.

He studied her pale face. "It could be a person you don't even know, I suppose. A clerk in a shop . . . a maid somewhere . . . some stranger who read about you . . ." His voice trailed off. Then, shaking his head. "No. I don't buy that. It's more personal."

She didn't answer. The panic was rising in her again. She felt its heat sting behind her eyes.

"Quinn! Don't just sit there. Help me. Think!"

"I've *been* thinking, Michael. I don't have any answers. I'd only been here four months when it started. I knew a lot of people very casually. As I do now. But no one very well."

"Then before here. In Washington, for instance. What about that? Could there have been someone there who read about your win? Who might have felt something against you?"

As always, when Washington was mentioned, there was that small wincing away. It showed on her face.

He stared at her intently. "Quinn?"

"There's no one, I tell you."

"Why did you throw up your job and come up here? I've always wondered. Elkhorn can't have much to offer you."

She thought of Jenny . . . the knowledge of her own failure . . . the bad nights after . . . the note to the Lakas family never answered . . . Lew Selby's importuning . . . the dull indoor job . . . hard, hating eyes on the buses every day . . . None of that had anything to do with what was happening now. Aloud, she said, "My job was boring. I was tired of city living, I guess." And wailing sirens, and blinking dome lights.

"When people tire of where they are, and up and leave, usually there's an immediate cause. Something they're running *from*."

Running from. Immediate cause. Jenny's death. But that had only been the last straw. It had all just added up. She hadn't been running away. She'd learned early that that never worked. You take with you wherever you go the person you are.

"You're not helping, Quinn."

"I don't know how to," she said.

His voice was level. "I don't believe you. There's something you haven't told me about. Every time I mention Washington there's a click inside of you. The curtain goes down, and you cut out."

"Nothing connected to this," she answered. Then: "I don't like being cross-examined, Michael."

"I think you should go back to Elkhorn. Take time off the job and stay put."

Her hand shook when she lifted the coffee cup to her lips. Her throat closed so that she could hardly swallow. It sounded good. To hide in Elkhorn. But how would that help? She whispered finally, "I'd feel like a sitting duck in Elkhorn."

"You don't have any clothes left with you."

She forced a faint smile. "I'll buy myself a new outfit in Ballston. A good excuse to be wildly extravagant." But she pushed her coffee aside. She had to get out of St. Mary's City for now. Put it behind her. Not think about it for a little while. Was that running away? Maybe. Just for the moment. She'd come back. She rose. "I'd better get ready to leave for Ballston."

Frightening images rose in Michael's mind as he went with her. The Rabbit overturned, smoking. A hand clenched around a knife, upraised. Fear roughened his voice. He said bluntly, "I tell you, Quinn, you've got to go back to Elkhorn. Give me a little time to see what I can find out."

She said stiffly, "I don't want to be told what I have to do."

"If you won't think for yourself, then you have to let me think for you."

She drew a deep shaky breath. Then: "Do you remember, when we were first together? I told you that you mustn't think it meant anything. I told you not to believe that I'd made a commitment to you."

"I remember it well," he retorted.

"I wanted you to know you had no obligation to me, nor I to you. That you had no rights. I had no rights."

Katherine, he thought. And laughed at himself. No. This was different. It was Quinn. He said evenly, "It was understood. But time has changed that."

"It hasn't. I don't want you to take care of me." Her hands were curled into small icy fists, her breath uneven. Away from St. Mary's City . . . on the road . . . away . . .

No use to argue further, he thought. He couldn't get past her defenses now. But she was scared. The thumbprints of fear under her eyes had become even darker. He'd have to work it out, and quickly. The beginning of it was already forming in his mind.

He helped her load the Rabbit. When he slammed the hatch, he took her into his arms, held her tightly for a moment. He felt her trembling. "You'll be careful, Quinn?"

"As careful as I know how to be." But her voice was shaking.

"And call me tonight in Elkhorn?" He paused. Added: "And if you don't get me there, then phone Helen?"

She nodded, not trusting herself to speak.

"And meanwhile, try to think . . ."

Again she nodded. She got into the Rabbit. She pulled out quickly. It crossed her mind that she could give up her job, immediately start on her trip. But that was no good. The danger followed her from Elkhorn to St. Mary's City, to Jewell's Landing. It could follow her anywhere. Better to wait where at least there was Michael. Someone who cared.

As she passed the city limits of St. Mary's City, she resolutely thought ahead. After Egypt, she would fly to— She imagined the globe of the world spinning beneath her father's fingers.

Michael watched until the Rabbit disappeared into a line of traffic. Then he moved quickly, knowing he'd have to if he were to catch up with her. He phoned Bill Sears and arranged to have his car picked up at the Capitol Hotel lot and returned to Elkhorn. He called Hertz and told them to have a Ford at the curb, running, when he got there.

Within twenty minutes, just at the outskirts of St. Mary's City, he had the Rabbit in view, and was keeping a list of the makes and plate numbers of the cars that followed the small green hatchback. He checked each off as it passed and went ahead, or if it left the highway.

One he checked was a dusty tan sedan that pulled over and made a U-turn.

Jerry, at the outskirts of St. Mary's City, heard the newscaster say, ". . . no further developments in the Herman shooting in Belair." And: "The sports world was shocked today . . ."

The memory of Adelaide Herman rose in his mind. Slim shoulders, clad in black silk. A pale and bruised white face under perfectly combed blond hair. A lucky one . . .

Whim pulled him over, drove him into a U-turn, led him back to St. Mary's City, and Belair.

He parked where he could see the luxurious Herman house, and settled back to wait. So rich, so lucky, so alive. Why Adelaide Herman, who had made herself a widow? Why should she breathe and love? He waited for the plan to flower in him. But nothing happened.

In a little while, his hand absently fell on the red silk blouse that lay on the seat beside him. He didn't know why he had stuffed it into his pocket. He just hadn't wanted to leave it behind. He was glad now.

It felt good. It made his fingers tingle. Flesh and soft silk were similar to the touch. He picked it up, held it to his nose. It smelled good, like the room.

Like Jenny's room. Not the two outside ones. The middle one. *Her* room. It smelled like her, he was sure. He remembered that smell. He had a cottony feeling in his mouth.

He was sleepy, the lids falling down over his eyes. The bed in Elkhorn was soft . . .

He started the car and drove away, the memory of Adelaide Herman hovering only faintly at the edges of his consciousness. He was leaving her now. But he'd be back. Just as he'd get back to Riverton and Mary Baker. Back to all the lucky ones, the winners, who had everything, and were alive. The ones whose time had come to die.

He touched the red blouse. First, always first, though, there was Quinn.

He put the blouse down and breathed deeply. He didn't know why he had done it. But it had been there, in his mind, every detail complete. The plastic card that easily opened the old locks in the hotel. A dress and skirt and blouse in the two outside rooms. And then, in *hers* . . .

His pants were suddenly, excruciatingly, too tight in the groin. *Her* room . . . the unmade bed, scented with her flesh . . . the damp towels in the bath . . .

Still, it wasn't enough. No. No, there would be more. He knew it. Sensed it. He had only to wait. There would be everything more. He had time. The money belt at his waist was thick with cash. He could do whatever he wanted. It would grow and flower and present itself to him. Mary Baker. Adelaide Herman. But first Quinn.

He felt that he was coming alive with the slow arrival of spring. He noticed that there was a greening in the meadows, and inches of day lily shoots were sprouting, clustered in unshaded places.

"Guess who?" the radio whispered softly to him. "He took an abandoned house and rebuilt it, and lived there alone for seven years. He was known as the Hermit of New England. He was ninety-one years old when he died. Guess who?" And, with a blare of trumpets: "The first caller with the correct answer will receive two tickets to *Madame Rosa,* with Simone Signoret, now playing at the Atheneum in St. Mary's City."

Jerry flipped to a different station. There was plenty of time, he thought. Seven years since Jenny turned against him and ran away. Plenty of time. All the rest of his life. It was okay. Surely it was working in him even now. Maybe by the time he arrived in Elkhorn he'd have the answer. He'd know what he was going to do. Until then he could lie in his bed and dream, waiting for Quinn to return on Friday night.

CHAPTER 19

Nathaniel Gordon surveyed his domain and found it good. The rug beside the cot warmed his feet when he rose in the morning. The camping blanket kept his bones comfortable by night.

The lantern gave him adequate light. The spirit stove gave him his meals. He missed only the chair and rosewood desk he had left at Roseview.

It had been easier than he had dared to imagine. Soon after talking to Tommy Galt at the bank, he had learned that the arrangements were made; his Social Security check was deposited as he'd wanted. A day later he packed his few belongings in two large grocery sacks and limped away from Roseview.

He left a note for Mrs. Leggette, saying that he was leaving for good, so that they wouldn't report him missing. He didn't tell them where he would be. But that would be okay. They had all he'd given to Beth Westlake in exchange for the lifetime care contract. With him gone, they'd have one more bed to sell. The walk to Windsor seemed easier than it had in years.

His room was ready to receive him. Over the month he had gotten what he needed. Harry Taylor, curious but too polite to ask, furnished Nathaniel with the crates he stood end on end, a board across them, to make a table. A makeshift wagon, painstakingly assembled from rusted rollerskate wheels and another board, transported the bed and stove from where they'd been bought in a garage sale.

Now Nathaniel straightened the blanket on the cot. His dish and cup were washed. His ties hung neatly from a wire hanger. The day's chores were done.

He put on a sweater and listened at the side door. No footsteps. No tires humming. No giggling children.

He was unsure of what would happen if the bank knew he was squatting in the back room. And he either lived rent-free or would have to go back to Roseview. This made him circumspect. It also confined him. Going in and out too often increased the risk. He varied the times, even the days, occasionally remaining indoors for forty-eight hours before venturing out again. That was one disadvantage of his new life.

The other was loneliness. Neither made him regret his decision to leave Roseview behind him.

As assured as he could be that he would exit unseen, he opened the door and slipped out. He made his way briskly behind the building and into a dirt alley, and from there into the street.

The sun was bright. Spring was in the air. Good for old bones. He grinned as he turned toward Taylor's Grocery.

The place wasn't crowded. Harry smiled at him. "Out for your constitutional, Nathaniel?"

"A good day for it."

Harry shoved a chair toward the older man. "If you've got time, sit."

Nathaniel seated himself, cane between his knees.

Harry checked out two customers. When they were gone, he said, "There's some day-old bread out back. In case you need any."

Nathaniel nodded his thanks. The day-old bread that Harry offered Nathaniel was usually fresh. Both men knew it. They both knew that the eggs Harry claimed he had to get rid of could actually have been sold. It was the grocer's way of helping. He was cautious in his offers. Nathaniel was cautious in returning the kindness.

Once weekly, since he had moved back, he'd bought a lottery ticket in the big jackpot draw. It was all he could do for his friend, and didn't amount to much, but at least it was something.

But today was Thursday. Nathaniel always bought the ticket on Friday. He considered. There was no real reason to stick to the routine. He bought his ticket, stuck it in his pocket. He'd forgotten about it by the time he started for home.

It was the following Thursday. The room was warm with the scented air of May.

Nathaniel sat in his chair, squinting at the newspaper in the light of the lantern.

The demonstrations against those nuclear power plants were continuing.

There was talk about oil off the coast of New Jersey.

The dollar had fallen again.

He wished he had a small radio. One of these days he'd save up enough to buy one at King's. A television set was out of the question. It was hard to keep up with the world. Maybe he could afford a sub-

scription to the *Atlantic Monthly*. Tommy Galt wouldn't mind if it came to the bank.

Nathaniel flipped the page.

The lottery number was in the lower left-hand corner. He glanced at it, shifting his eyes to the right to read a tiny item about a volcanic eruption in the Pacific Ocean.

The blurred afterimage of the colors and numbers remained in his mind. Red 11 Green 21 Blue 25.

He dismissed the faint suspicion that the series was a familiar one. All numbers seemed familiar, all colors, too. He read a short paragraph about a shooting in St. Mary's City. Then, with a sigh, he gave in to the troubled feeling he had.

He took his wallet from his breast pocket, drew the black and white and silver card from between two single dollar bills. Red 11 Green 21 Blue 25.

His breath shuddered in his throat. The skin at his fingertips was suddenly numb, while his face felt afire. The shaking of his body sent the cane that leaned against his hip skittering away.

"I've won something," he croaked aloud to the dim room. "By all that's holy, I've won."

He had no idea then what that small bit of cardboard with its ragged edge of foil was worth to him. He didn't know what he'd won.

He told himself that it could wait until the next day. He was tired. Maybe he oughtn't to go out. But he couldn't concentrate. He couldn't finish reading the newspaper. He was too excited to consider the chores preliminary to fixing his supper. He limped slowly back and forth across the small room, until, with a shake of his head, he readied himself for the street.

He went through the usual routine of listening at the door before he went out, and made his usual detour along the way.

Taylor's was still open. Harry gave him a surprised look. "Anything wrong, Nathaniel?"

"I wanted you to see this." Nathaniel thrust the ticket and newspaper side by side under Harry's nose.

The grocer looked, blinked, said hoarsely, "They match."

"You think it'll maybe give me a television set?" Nathaniel asked.

Small beads of sweat broke out on Harry's forehead. A wave of red rose into his cheeks. A slow grin exposed his yellowed teeth. He took a thick pamphlet from beneath the counter, studied it, nodded.

He went to the back of the store, returned with a straight chair. "Sit," he said.

"What for? I can stand on my feet. What's the matter with you?"

"Sit," Harry repeated. He pressed Nathaniel, still protesting, into the chair. "Nathaniel, listen, you didn't win a television set. It's more."

"Is it?" Nathaniel chuckled. "Well, I don't need a Chris-Craft. Although I guess maybe I could sell one."

"Nathaniel, it isn't a Chris-Craft. It's money. A lot of money. You've pulled off a win in the three-month jackpot draw."

"All right. What does it give me?"

Harry sighed. "I guess there's no easy way. You better try to control yourself, though. You just got two hundred thousand dollars." He went on quickly. "The government'll take twenty percent, and I'll get one percent. So it's not really two hundred thousand, so you just relax now."

Nathaniel was speechless. A glint slowly grew in his pale blue eyes. A small smile settled on his mouth. At last he said, "That's real money, isn't it, Harry?"

"It is." Then: "What're you going to do with it?"

Nathaniel rose to his feet, leaned on his cane. "This takes some considering." But he already knew what he planned. It was only a matter of how to accomplish it. First to locate Beth Westlake, who was working somewhere in one of the southern counties.

"Let me validate your signature for you right now," Harry said.

"What's that?"

"So they'll know you're you when it's time for them to pay off." Harry rummaged under the counter again, pulled out a rumpled form. He squinted at it, then took up a pen and filled it in, but when he came to "claimant's address," he read it aloud, and raised his eyes.

"The bank," Nathaniel said quickly.

"It won't matter now," Harry told him. "You can move to the fanciest hotel in town."

"I won't want to move," Nathaniel retorted. And he added quickly, "I don't know what you're talking about."

Harry grinned, printed the bank's address. "Okay." And passing the form: "Sign."

Nathaniel did, watched as Harry stapled the ticket and form together. "Now?"

"You put it in this envelope and drop it into the mailbox outside. You'll hear from the Lottery Commission pretty soon."

"You won't tell anybody?"

"*I* won't. But you're not going to be able to keep it a secret."

"It's nobody's business but mine."

"Nope. But everybody's going to be interested."

Five days later. A Wednesday. Nathaniel was at the bank. There had been stares, whispers, a good deal of what Nathaniel considered to be unnecessary handshaking.

Tom Galt grinned, gave him a letter from the State Lottery Commission, said, "Somebody to see you, Mr. Gordon."

The "somebody" was a skinny young man who introduced himself in a slur of words that Nathaniel didn't get, and who blinded him with a quickly lifted camera, which Nathaniel didn't like. The young man ignored his protest, said, "Thanks. For the *Commission News,*" and "Goodbye. Somebody'll be in touch," as he disappeared through the tall bronze doors.

"Something wrong?" Tom Galt inquired, seeing Nathaniel's frown.

"My business," Nathaniel answered, and thought of Harry Taylor. It appeared the grocer was going to be right.

But five quiet days passed.

Nathaniel had refused to talk to the somebody from the Lottery Commission, and had avoided going to the bank lest he be entrapped there. His check came, with the deductions Harry had told him about. Tom Galt sent word via Harry, so Nathaniel knew when to go in and make the biggest deposit he had ever made in his life.

The next afternoon, as he stepped into the grocery store, Harry said, "Nathaniel, your secret's out," and offered him a copy of the Windsor *Leader*.

The picture was a flattering one. Nathaniel's face was lit with a beatific smile. His hair was in place. His thick brows were straight. The caption named him as the seventy-seven-year-old winner of the trimonthly draw, said he had refused an interview but described him as a local man, retired from his own business on Bailey Road.

"How on earth—" Nathaniel began.

"They took it out of the *Commission News*." Harry produced the newest copy. It listed winners by category. Nathaniel Gordon, May winner of the trimonthly jackpot draw, aged seventy-seven, was a category all his own.

Within a day Nathaniel was known to millions of newspaper readers, television watchers, and radio listeners.

One of them was Mrs. Lenore Leggette, administrator of the Roseview Home for the Elderly.

Another was Jerry Lakas. He was lying on his bed, drifting. The transistor beside him whispered, "Nathaniel Gordon, aged seventy-seven, of Windsor, retired from his business on Bailey Road, has won the jackpot draw of two hundred thousand dollars."

The words sank gently into Jerry's consciousness.

Nathaniel Gordon. Seventy-seven years old. Old. An old man. A man much like Jerry's own father. ALIVE, and rich. And what did he need it for? The life—why did that withered old stinking decaying body need the life? And the money, too? Why should he be alive and have all that money? Why? When Jenny was dead.

CHAPTER 20

Mrs. Leggette checked with the State Lottery Commission and was given the Windsor bank as Nathaniel's address. She went there and was told that the bank did not give out information about its clients. She protested to Tom Galt, but he shrugged, repeating the policy, although he was certain Nathaniel was squatting in the Bailey Street store the bank now owned.

Mrs. Leggette gave up for the moment and returned to Roseview to consider her next step. Two hundred thousand dollars was a great deal of money for an old man to manage. She was determined, she told herself, to protect Nathaniel Gordon from the unscrupulous, who would soon be descending in droves upon him.

That same day Nathaniel came to talk to Tom Galt about what he wanted to do with his winnings. He described National Nursing Homes Company and its policies at Roseview. He was determined to buy Roseview from NNHC and locate Beth Westlake to run it for him as it had always been run.

Tom grinned, agreed to see what he could do.

When Nathaniel left the bank he passed a dusty tan sedan parked at the corner. He didn't notice it then, nor did he realize that it followed him down Bailey Street.

Much later, unaware of the eyes that peered balefully at him through the high window, he sat in his chair.

He was content with the day's doing, but he was tired. He was too tired to fix a bowl of soup for his supper, even to turn on the radio.

He rested, a frail hand on the cane that leaned against his thigh, and considered lighting the lantern. But even that seemed to involve more effort than he cared to expend. Besides, a silvery trail of moonlight made a path across the red carpet near his cot.

Dozing, he thought of Mrs. Leggette and how surprised she would be when NNHC sold Roseview out from under her. A smile touched his lips when he envisioned Beth Westlake back where she belonged.

He heard a faint sound beyond the door, but paid no attention to it. There were always sounds coming in from outside.

But suddenly the room brightened with more moonlight. The door swung open, slow, soundless. A tall dark figure was outlined by the glow of sky behind it.

"Who's that?" Nathaniel demanded.

There was no answer. But reflections shone from rimless glasses. Brilliant holes where eyes should have been.

"What do you want?" Nathaniel demanded.

The dark figure advanced into the room. The door closed.

Nathaniel rose, gripping his cane. A quick pulse beat behind his right ear. Another pounded in his throat. He said, "If it's the money, you've come to the wrong place. The bank's got it."

"Money," Jerry Lakas whispered angrily. "Money. That's all you can think of. Counting the cash in the register, then looking sideways at me. Money!"

"Then what do you want?" Nathaniel asked, aware now of a chill in his toes, his fingertips, a trembling in the hand that gripped the cane.

The man that Jerry stared at, heart burning with hate, blurred and shaded into Mortimer Lakas. Jerry saw his father before him, and spoke to him.

"It was your fault, Pa. You gave her to me. You said she was mine. And then you wanted her yourself. That was it, wasn't it? You wanted her for yourself. So she ran away."

"What're you talking about?" Nathaniel muttered through numbing lips. "Who ran away? Who did I want?"

"Old," Jerry retorted. "Old. Old. It's time for you to die, damn you!" He lunged forward, jerked the cane from Nathaniel, flung it away.

Nathaniel staggered, off balance. He flung his numbed hands outward, grasping unsubstantial air. Slowly, in long spinning moments, his legs folded under him, and he fell.

The silvery room whirled. There was the sound of rolling thunder under the silence, and of close-by drums pounding in uneven rhythm. He saw an eyeless face hang over him, teeth bared beneath snarling lips. He saw rising red mists, and far far away a flickering light . . .

Jerry watched as Nathaniel's eyes widened in a fixed stare that saw nothing. Pink rings appeared around the frozen pupils and spread. His mouth hung open, drawn to the left, and from it there came long slow struggling breaths, with long slow pauses between them.

One of those pauses lengthened. The room remained still.

Jerry grinned, let himself out into the dark alley.

In a little while he crawled into his bed in the Inland Motel. He was thinking of all those lucky ones who were still alive. And how he would kill them. It would come. He'd know how. Just as he'd known how for the old man. He fell asleep weeping for Jenny.

The following Sunday night.

There was only light traffic on the Old North Road. The neon signs at Cory's Wine and Liquor, and at Fieldstone's Supermarket, were out. But the dinner-hour business at the Burger Barn was brisk. A line of cars rolled slowly from its driveway. Among them was a dusty tan sedan. It, like the others, paused for the yield sign. Then it whipped out, passed the two ahead of it, and spun into the highway, tires screeching. At the State Police substation it slowed briefly. Beyond, it picked up speed again.

Jerry's hands were white-knuckled tight on the wheel. Sweat beaded his face and chilled his armpits. He didn't know why he had suddenly shoved aside his half-eaten hamburger with slaw and Russian dressing. He didn't know why he had hurried outside to go speeding to the dirt track off Westbrook Road. He had been adrift, waiting. Then the impulse struck.

The car jounced on the track. He watched for rocks by the light of the moon, unaware of the still-cool evening, but shivering.

The hill rose up before him. Moments later, he had arrived. The car was deep in the old vine-hung shed, tucked away where no stray reflection of glass or chrome could flash through the dark.

He made a circuit of the place. Windows boarded tight. Doors nailed, but easy to open. It proved unnecessary. At the back he stumbled over a cellar entrance. Flush with the ground. Two wing doors matted with the dead and withered leaves of a lilac bush nearby.

He explored the inside of the house briefly. Three floors. Rooms dark as caves. He lost interest.

Outside again, he leaned on a rusted pump, one more among the many shadows. He stared down the hill, across the meadow and above the budding trees. From that vantage he had a clear view of the house on Old Barn Road.

CHAPTER 21

The same Sunday evening.

Quinn and Michael walked along the hard-packed sand, trying to skirt the long white crests that rolled in. Finally, when their shoes were wet, they took them off, and went barefooted.

But it was cold. She said so. Michael told her that the ocean was much warmer in September.

She shivered only partly from the chill salt breeze that spun through the cliff-encircled shore. September. Would she be in Cambodia looking at Angkor Wat? Or in Mandalay, in Burma? It wouldn't be with Michael. She was glad when he suggested that they leave. The sunset was fading. The cliffs' shadows lengthening.

They put on their wet footwear, and made the slow climb up the rocks.

Michael watched her move ahead of him. He'd have to tell her soon. Any time, once they were back at the house, she could hear of it on the news. One more question. At least he'd be able to reassure her.

He decided to take her back to Old Barn Road to change to dry things. Afterward they'd return to his place for the dinner he had prepared that morning.

In the car, he said, "Something happened in Windsor, Quinn. To Nathaniel Gordon. He died Friday night. A man from his bank found him yesterday afternoon. It was a cerebral hemorrhage."

Her lips whitened, pressed together. Her hands folded into a single tight shaking fist. "Poor man. He was so happy. He was going to have his Roseview again." And, in a near whisper: "I wonder if—if he had letters, too."

"No."

She raised a brow, her eyes doubtful.

"No," Michael repeated firmly. "I called Lacy Pickett as soon as I heard. He found out for me. The police had searched his room very carefully. There was nothing. No letters. Just his will. He left his money to a woman named Beth Westlake. They talked to the man at the bank, and some friends of his on the street. Nathaniel wasn't worried. And nothing out-of-the-way turned up."

She nodded. But the doubt remained in her eyes.

Michael knew that she was thinking that Nathaniel Gordon had been a big winner. And he had died. Maybe he'd never even known that some evil stranger was tracking him.

But *she* knew. Someone *was* tracking her.

Michael knew it, too. He had gone to work on the problem as if it were a story he was developing. Since the terrifying incident with the clothes in St. Mary's City, he'd spent days riding after her in rented cars. He'd been unable to find a trace of *A Friend*. He'd inquired about new people in Elkhorn and environs. He'd devised a calendar that began with the first letter, and where it came from, and went through the tire-slashing, the killing of the cat named Devil. Then on to what happened at the Capitol Hotel in St. Mary's City. He saw that it was building. Building to danger for Quinn.

After Quinn changed, they set out for Michael's.

He told himself that he must wait until dinner was over before talking about it again.

He was unaware of being watched from the abandoned house on the hill as he drove out of Old Barn Road.

They were having brandy.

Michael said, "I might be able to catch up with you in September."

"No, Michael. When I go, it has to be over."

"Like when you left Washington. That was over, too, wasn't it? According to you. But I don't think so. If you'd only give me some idea—"

"We've covered that ground before. It didn't help."

"It's got to be a grudge thing. A hate thing."

She rose to poke the logs in the fireplace.

"Let me," he told her.

"I can do it."

He managed to grin. "You say that about everything. It was about the first word or two you told me when we met."

She frowned, remembering. JESUS SAVES, JE for Jenny. Then: "Didn't I tell you the Rabbit was hung up?"

"That came after." And: "First there was something about the oil pan."

"It threw you, didn't it?" she said, smiling.

"Nearly."

He took the poker from her. "So, if you don't mind . . ."

She returned to sit on the sofa.

When he went to join her, he decided it was time to get back to the subject of danger. And where it could be coming from. Such as Washington.

But she moved closer, settled into his arms. He smoothed the silken hair on her shoulders. Later, he told himself.

They kissed, the warmth of the fire washing over them. Soon they rose, clinging to each other, and went, without speaking, into the porch. The shaggy limbs of the spruce whispered against the window as they sank down to the bed.

Again, as always, their coming together was easy and natural and right. He felt her silken length against him, and the play of muscles in her back and legs, and the warmth of her breasts on his flesh. The sweetness of her scent enveloped him.

But there was more. A new driving desperation. Her hands raked his shoulders. Burning trails where the nails dug in. Her teeth nibbled his mouth. He had to clench against explosion. To force himself to wait, wait. He crushed her to him, so they both lost breath. Their bones seemed to touch through shields of sensitized skin. He put his lips to her nipples. They were already engorged. As he himself was engorged. Full. Ready. Wanting. He suckled one hot nipple, then the other, and felt her tongue delicately stroke the shell of his ear.

With a wordless murmur, she broke away from him. A nudge at his hip. He rolled to one side. Her mouth was at his bellybutton. Her hands at his groin, and moving in butterfly touches.

He pulled her over him, her weight on his, blanketing him with spreading heat. A shift. His weight on her. Her thighs opened. Welcomed. A whispered gasp as they joined. Her body tightened, drew him deeper. Again he clamped down, waiting. But mutual urgency lifted and drove them. A throbbing timelessness. A silken sinking. Rest. Returning breath.

Then her hands were on him again. A swift fire licked at him. A touch that turned him. She was astride. Quick hard thrusts. The caress of her hands . . . The silken fall of her hair on his mouth . . .

Jerry clung with one trembling arm to the tree trunk, his hand clawing its rough bark. His other hand burrowed inside his pants, and stroked, and pulled and squeezed. His eyes were wide, staring. He breathed in deep hard gasps.

They were of molten gold, the two of them, aglow in the light that shone on the bed. Their bodies twisted and turned and humped and rolled.

Jerry was there, too. Over her, thrusting.

He was beneath her, enclosed in her shimmering flesh.

She moved. Her lips slid down his body past breast and belly button, and into his groin. Her mouth encircled the fiery point, and sucked there. Jenny! Jenny! His Jenny. . . .

His breath became a whispered keening. Fire turned into flame, and his bones shook in his flesh, and his vision blurred. An instant's unconsciousness. He clung to the tree, with its shaggy limbs trembling around him. Sweat poured from him in the cool air of the spring night. It smelled like blood.

When Quinn stirred, Michael partly awakened. But he let himself drift, listening as she moved across the room.

It was easy to pretend then. They were man and wife. She was rising to shower, would soon return to him. All the hours in his empty existence would be filled by her.

She drew on her skirt, wondering at how Michael had changed her. The passion she understood, though he had been the first man she had known to bring it to her. A soft melting satiety still lingered in her body. But even more was the freedom to ask for, to give. The shared awareness that replaced a sense of self.

Could she give that up? Give Michael up?

Michael stirred. "Quinn?"

"I'm here," she answered. But she moved farther from him. She leaned an elbow on the windowsill.

"I'm thinking of the Great Wall," he said.

"China." Then, briskly, "Someday I'll see it. The doors will open again, and I'll be there."

"The wall between us," he told her. "The doors will open there, too."

But she wondered. How many chances do you take with your life? How many times do you learn how you can fail?

The shaggy limbs of the spruce whispered against the window again. They nearly covered it. Through them she glimpsed a few distant stars.

Closer, so close that she felt almost able to touch it, there hung among the drooping limbs a big white blur, a fruit of the night, planes and shadows oddly human and familiar.

Breath held, eyes widening, she stared at it.

A wind rustled. The blur swung, drifted in a quarter turn. What hung there in the shadows was no longer some strange fruit of the night nor flower too early for May. It was a human face. And no longer just familiar. It was known. *Known.* Chestnut hair. High-bridged nose. Square chin.

"Jenny!" she gasped, falling back.

The face slipped from view as she turned, screaming, "Jenny's at the window!"

Michael leaped from the bed, lunged toward Quinn.

"There, looking in"—her voice shook with terror—"it's impossible! Because she's dead. I saw her with my own eyes, Michael. I held her hand. Surely she was dead!"

Michael jerked on his trousers, charged for the door, and out into the dark of the overgrown garden. He heard a rustling at the side of the house and dashed that way. Ahead of him there was a sharp thunk, a blow against wood. He threw himself at the spruce that covered the sleeping-porch window.

He caught a glimpse of Quinn peering down at him through the glass, and stubbed his toe on a rock. He knew instantly that he had been duped. Whoever had been there only moments before had fled. Thrown the rock against the house to make Michael believe he was close by.

Even as Quinn cried out to him, Michael spun away. From far off, through the brush, he heard the sound of a motor, the spinning of wheels as a car roared off down Dayman Lane toward the highway.

Inside he found Quinn still leaning at the window.

She turned, her face pale, her eyes as dark as the night. "Someone was there. You oughtn't to have gone out."

"I wish I'd been smarter and faster."

She shuddered. "Michael, no!" Then: "I couldn't have imagined it. Could I?"

"I know you didn't. I heard running footsteps, and then a car."

She pressed small fists to her temples. "Then I'm not altogether crazy."

"No, Quinn." The use of intuition proved. Danger to Quinn. Close, always coming closer. A stranger's eyes watching as they made love. Then, gently: "Quinn, who is Jenny?"

"That's the thing. I couldn't have seen *her.*"

"But who did you think you saw? Who's Jenny?"

"Jenny Lakas. But Michael, Michael, I must have dreamed it. I must have. She died last August. She couldn't have been here, looking in the window."

"But someone was. Hang on to that much."

Quinn drew a deep breath, straightened her shoulders. She was Quinn Monroe. She would deal with this. Whatever it was. She said, "Perhaps the shadows . . . the way the light fell . . ."

"You could have mistaken who you saw. But not that you saw someone."

He thought of calling the State Police substation to report a Peeping Tom. But the man was long gone now. And such a report would bring in cars. Elkhorn was a small town. By morning people would be asking in Fieldstone's what Quinn Monroe was doing at the Dayman house in the middle of the night. He decided to let it go for now.

Watching, he saw her withdraw into her usual calm. It was a visible thing, the signs of it slight, yet because he knew her so well he realized what was happening.

The frown smoothed away from between her dark brows, and a slight smile tilted her mouth. Her hands loosened and fell away from her face. Her shoulders squared and braced. Finally she said, "It was my unknown friend, wasn't it, Michael?"

"It was at least a Peeping Tom," he answered.

Quick color stained her cheeks. "He had a great deal to peek at."

"To hell with him. I asked you before: What about this Jenny Lalas? Why did you think you'd seen her at the window?"

"Jenny's been dead since August." Quinn was remembering pain even as she spoke. She turned from Michael.

"Stay with me, Quinn."

"Not tonight. I'll rest better in my own bed." Alone. Without his warmth beside her. Without the weakness his closeness brought her to.

But, once at home, she found no rest. She wandered the silent room, listening to the squeaks and sighs of the old barn.

Jenny? Impossible.

Then who? Why?

Still asking herself those questions, Quinn set out for Jewell's Landing via Passamody and the Coastal Road early the next morning.

"I hope I didn't awaken you," Michael said.

"Me? I've been painting since seven. Good light." Helen ran her stained fingers through her wild hair, waved him in. "Come have coffee." She paused, the door half shut. "But Quinn's gone, you know."

Snowball rubbed against his ankle. He picked up the cat. "I want to talk to you, Helen."

Shrewd eyes studied him from middle-aged pouches. "About Quinn," Helen said finally. "Okay. Have a seat." When she had served him, she took a chair at the other side of the table. "What's wrong? You look grim."

"Tell me about Jenny Lakas."

Helen opened her mouth, closed it. Then: "Why do you want to know? What about her?"

"Do you have to know my reason?"

"I guess I don't. But I'm surprised Quinn's never told you. I imagined she had."

He shook his head.

"She's never wanted to talk to me about Jenny either. God knows I tried to get her to. I thought it would do her good."

"But you know about Jenny, don't you?"

"Just a little. From Irene Harrich. My cousin. She wrote me that Jenny had committed suicide. And I didn't even hear that until Quinn had been settled in with me for several weeks."

"Who was Jenny?"

"Quinn's roommate, apartment mate. She killed herself in August. It upset Quinn."

"That's all you know?"

Helen shrugged. "That's it."

Michael got to his feet. "I'd like to get in touch with your cousin."

"Do you think what happened back there's got anything to do with Quinn's troubles here?"

"Maybe."

"It's pretty farfetched, Michael."

"If it is, it'll only be a short waste of time."

Helen rose, rummaged under the kitchen sink, and came up with a wilted address book. She handed it to him. "Under H."

He quickly copied the address and phone number.

"Daytimes you can reach her at National Roadway Users. That's the same place Quinn used to work. I don't have that number."

"Information will."

"I doubt Irene will know much more than she wrote me. Quinn's not a talker."

"No," he agreed, starting for the door.

"She'll be leaving next month. Maybe it'll resolve itself when she does."

"Maybe." But he was afraid it wouldn't. He felt that the threat had followed her from Washington. It could follow her again.

"Are you really going to let her go?" Helen demanded.

"Not without me. If I can help it," he said gruffly, and went out to his car.

First things first. What was it about Jenny Lakas that made Quinn imagine she had seen the girl when she looked into the face of a Peeping Tom? What had happened in Washington that brought the frozen look to Quinn whenever the city was mentioned?

He turned left onto the Old North Road, drove past the Rolls-Royce dealership and parked at the State Police substation.

Lacy Pickett was on duty. Michael asked, "Do you remember a girl named Quinn Monroe? She won a lottery, and received some anonymous letters as a result of the publicity?"

Lacy grinned. "Could I forget her, Mike? A pretty girl like that?"

Michael went on to describe what had happened since the letters stopped, ended with, "I can't believe in that much coincidence. Can you?"

By then, Lacy's grin was gone. "No," he answered. "I can't. From unsigned letters mailed first in Kansas City to a Peeping Tom at your house last night. No. It's too much to ask any man to believe. Even though it probably is just what you called it. A coincidence."

"You're not serious."

"I am, Mike. We've had a rash of animal killings, and small outbreaks of vandalism. There's always a couple of Peeping Toms around. Take a look at the blotter, if you don't believe me."

"I'm certain there's more to this."

"Being certain's not enough." Lacy paused. Then: "Is this business with your girl the reason you asked me about the old man dying up in Windsor?"

Michael nodded.

"Because they'd both won big in the lotteries?"

"Yes."

"You really are stretching, aren't you? A seventy-seven-year-old man . . . Look at the actuarial tables, for God's sake."

"Quinn's in danger."

The trooper shook his head. "I'd help if I could. But what is there to do? The letters weren't traceable when I looked at them, and still aren't. There were no witnesses to the tire-slashing, none to what happened to the cat. Three ladies were affected by what happened in St. Mary's City. Your Peeping Tom made a clean getaway. So . . ." He spread his hands. "If we had more men we could maybe put somebody on her. But for how long? Or maybe you can get a man up from Boston, though the same would hold true for him."

"I tried to spot somebody following her. It was no good." Michael rose. "I've got a small lead. I guess I'll go ahead and follow that out. Then maybe I'll get back to you."

"Anytime," Lacy said. "You know that, Mike."

Michael explained to Irene Harrich that he was a friend of Quinn's, and calling from Elkhorn. Then: "I wonder, did you know her roommate, Jenny Lakas?"

"I met her a few times," Irene answered, in a bewildered tone. "But why are you asking me about her?"

"Can you tell me anything about her?"

"Not really. And Quinn didn't say much about her. I think that's what got Quinn so upset afterward. Realizing that she knew so little about Jenny. As if not knowing were abnormal or something. But it isn't. Not in Washington. But Quinn took it hard. Anyway, later, I told her about my cousin in Elkhorn, so Quinn decided she'd try it for a while. And off she went. Who'd have thought she'd win a hundred thousand dollars just because of that?"

"You said Quinn didn't know anything about Jenny. What do you mean?"

"Where she came from. Who her people were. Why Jenny killed herself. But it turned out all right. Jenny *did* have people in Kansas. Her body was shipped home. And her things. And Quinn made a change. So that was the end of that."

Not quite, Michael thought. Quinn still imagined that she saw dead Jenny's face. And someone hated Quinn for being lucky, being alive.

He asked, "You did say Kansas, didn't you? Not Kansas City?"

"Kansas. A town named Kenyon. I remember because I used to live on Kenyon Street. But you do intrigue me, Michael Dayman. I've a good mind to call Quinn and ask her what it's all about."

"I'd appreciate it if you didn't. At least not yet."

He put down the phone, knocking over a stack of tapes as he did.

He left them where they fell. Damn the book! All the urgency he had felt when he began it was gone. Doc Po Ram. A slight man, wearing a uniform. The carbine raised, trained at the legs of the bound prisoner. The sudden earshattering series of blasts. A bloody body falling one way. Legs flying through the air in red showers. And years later, a small paragraph in *The New York Times* that caught Michael's attention, made him wonder what had happened to Doc Po Ram, the others like him. Urgency to know born in that moment. The manuscript begun. It meant nothing now.

There was only Quinn.

He crossed to the bookshelf. He took down the largest atlas he had, and turned to a map of the United States. Kenyon, Kansas. He found it at once. An inch away, by scale some fourteen miles, there was Kansas City, where the first few of the anonymous letters had been mailed.

His hunch had been right. It had begun in Washington. But Jenny Lakas was dead. She'd been sent home to Kenyon to be buried.

Within a few minutes he was on the All-State, heading south to Boston.

About then, Quinn was just finishing up her day's work in Jewell's Landing.

CHAPTER 22

Joe Nighthawk looked from the caretaker to the mountain of rotting drywall and sacks of decaying garbage. "Twenty-five bucks! It'll take the day."

The caretaker was thin as a fence post, but bent in the middle, as if, sometime, his back had been broken. "That's what the man told me," he said.

Twenty-five dollars was better than a fucking nothing. Joe nodded, turned his head for a deep breath of moist salty air, and waded in.

He maneuvered a stinking barrel onto the truck. He grappled with a bale of soggy newspapers and slung it in a short arc. It landed with a thud. Its tie rope disintegrated. So did the bale. "Son of a bitch!" Joe turned his back. He held his breath while he moved a cardboard box of eggshells and orange rinds peppered with moist coffee grounds.

When the mountain of garbage had been transferred from the yard to the truck, he accepted his money and got behind the wheel.

The truck bucked and fought him. He listened to its wheezes and whines, mouthing a stream of obscenities, with a worried frown on his face. It couldn't break down now. The stink was all around him. He had to make it to the town dump.

He was momentarily distracted when a motorcycle sped past him. The driver was helmeted. Clinging to him, with her butt hanging over the pinion, was a girl with long wild blond hair. Joe wondered if she was getting a tickle in her clit with every bounce, and whether the driver would profit by those tickles later. Goddamn, she was one wild-looking woman.

But Joe had other things on his mind. Geraldine had been looking in the cupboard when he left the house. She could make a christening gown from an old blouse for the new grandson. But she couldn't cook a meal out of nothing and a stone. He hadn't given her a dollar in over two weeks. He wanted to hand her the twenty-five for grocery shopping before he went to the dump.

The truck wheezed its way down the highway, Joe handling it gently, swearing when somebody pulled up behind him, blasted an imperial horn. Jesus, Mary, and Joseph! The dumb sucking son of a bitch! Didn't he know that Joe, too, would like to be driving a Chrysler?

He slowed. There was a tan sedan just ahead of him. Ahead of that an apple-green Rabbit that suddenly developed a wobble . . .

Quinn felt the vibration, heard the plop of rubber on macadam. A flat. Swearing, she pulled over. She had two girls to see at the southern end of the cove. She wasn't dressed for changing a tire.

A tan sedan drifted close, slowed.

She remembered the Rabbit squatting amid debris in St. Mary's City, and was suddenly frightened. A pulse hammered in her throat. Cold sweat gathered on her face.

A battered, coughing pickup truck swung in.

The tan sedan flashed away.

Joe Nighthawk climbed from behind the wheel, blinked at Quinn. She was one goddamn pretty girl, and wouldn't he like to hump her? Only pale. Skittish. Standing well away from him. Not that he blamed her, the way he stank. But she looked scared. He said reassuringly, "It's okay, lady. Only a flat. I'll change her for you."

She nodded at him, opened the hatch, and he set to work quickly. One goddamn pretty girl all right. But he couldn't waste time imagining how she'd be without clothes. He was worried about getting the pickup started again.

When he was finished, she offered him five dollars. He was tempted to refuse it. A pretty girl like that. Only he needed it. Five dollars added to twenty-five made for thirty. And thirty was better than nothing, too.

Quinn drove away, telling herself that anybody who was on the road as much as she was was bound to have a flat tire sometime.

Joe got into the pickup, nursed the starter until it caught, and went on with a relieved sigh.

The turnoff that was as familiar to him as his own face came on him suddenly. He braked hard and just barely made it.

A faint white mist drifted against his windshield. He frowned. There wasn't any mist about. Too early still. A wreath of white dribbled upward, floated above the radiator, then spotted the cracked glass in front of him. Goddamn! Overheating.

A good thing he was nearly home. Maybe the radiator needed water.

As he stopped at the side of the house, there was more steam around the front end of the pickup. He grabbed his gloves and jumped out. There was a sudden jarring explosion. He stared while steam poured from the bottom of the pickup, billowing up through the rusted grillwork at the front end.

Geraldine came and stood on the back step. She said nothing, just shook her head.

He grinned sourly, brought her the thirty dollars. "You got your grocery list made up?"

She nodded. "Where'd you get that load of garbage?"

"Up to Hardy Road."

"What're you going to do with it?"

"Jesus, Mary, and Joseph, Geraldine! What in the hell would I do with it except take it to the fucking dump?"

"Joe," she murmured, pained and disapproving.

She hated the language. Usually he was careful around her. Now he was just too aggravated to care.

She looked at him. She looked at the pickup.

"Christ, I don't know," he said. "Don't ask me. I think it's the radiator."

"How long you going to leave that stinking mess next to the house?"

He sighed deeply. It was fucking bad. No use pretending it wasn't. Even the three dogs had backed off into the shadows under the bushes. "I guess I'll burn it," he told her.

She smiled at him before she went in. "Thanks, Joe."

He released the brake, and pushed and shoved and sweated and swore, until he rolled the pickup deeper into the yard. Then he got a shovel and moved the trash off. By the time he was through, it was deep dark and the fog had begun to move in. The horns wailed in the cove, and buoy beacons flashed their signals to the sky.

He swore and sweated again, pushing the truck well away, although he was inclined to leave it and let it go up with the rest of the trash. It would have satisfied his mood to see it blast off in a big boom. But he knew he'd be sorry after.

He set the trash ablaze, and stood watching the flames leap up, the odorous smoke billow thickly and spread. In the brightness he saw the ghost outline of his boat, aglitter with sun and lobster shell.

A red blink interfered. He turned as the dogs raced in, barking. He yelled at them to sit, and went toward the patrol car as a policeman stepped out.

They exchanged a long silent look.

"What're you doing?" the policeman asked finally. His face was pink in the firelight. His eyes were round, blue, cold as fish belly.

"You can see," Joe answered.

"You ever hear about the antipollution laws of this state and this county and this township?"

"I guess so." Motherfucking goddamn cop, Joe thought. "Anybody complaining?"

"I am." The policeman coughed on bitter smoke. "You can maybe get away with this on the reservation. Only not around here."

Joe explained about the pickup.

"Whatever, you can't burn that stuff within town limits. Jewell's Landing isn't some reservation."

Joe said, "I can't carry it to the dump with my truck busted."

The policeman took a book out of his pocket. "Name?"

"What're you doing?"

"I'm writing you a citation that means you're going to pay thirty bucks for burning trash in town limits." The policeman looked at Joe hard, waited.

Joe closed his teeth on his lower lip. His jaw was rock. His black eyes smoked as hot as the fire behind him.

Finally he gave his name and address and handed over the truck registration.

After a moment's study, the policeman returned it. "Pretty soon you Indians are going to say you don't even need these papers." When Joe didn't rise to the bait, the man went on. "Okay. Now get that fire out."

"What'll I do with what's left?"

"That's your worry. But if you leave it, you'll end up with another citation. For having a dump in your back yard." The policeman gave the place a long slow look, then turned and left.

Joe shoveled dirt on the fire until it was a vast smoking pile.

When he went inside, he grumbled, "Goddamn motherfucking cop."

Geraldine gave him a pained look again, but offered him the thirty dollars he had given her.

"Buy your groceries with it," he said.

"And how'll you pay their lousy fine?"

"I'll tell them I don't have it."

"And go to jail."

"You'll still have the groceries."

"I guess so." She smiled at him. "Listen, I'm in the middle of ironing. Take five bucks and go down and get you some beers. Then come back for me. Okay?"

It was the best idea he'd heard all week. That was one sweet woman, his Geraldine. He didn't argue. He got a lift almost in front of the house and thought that maybe his luck was changing.

He had two beers at Henley's, leaning against the bar. He listened to the talk of his friends. Pogie, Frenchy, Nick the Greek. They were trading the same old fucking stories about their wins. They went back and forth, buying small lottery tickets in the instant games, yelling when they won a dollar, whooping when they lost.

After a while, Joe got tired of watching. He took one out of the few singles he had left, got himself a ticket. He carefully scraped the foil off at a corner of the design. A dollar sign appeared. He went on. Another dollar sign. That was good. He stopped breathing, and rubbed his nail quickly at the two remaining squares. Dollar signs! Bingo!

"Hey, look! Jesus, Mary, and Joseph, I got something!"

"One hundred bucks," Pogie said, and turning: "You hear that, guys? Joe just won himself a hundred bucks."

Joe stood still. He'd been right. His luck was finally changing.

"What you going to do with it?" Pogie demanded.

A hundred bucks. It seemed like a fortune. He saw sacks of groceries, and Geraldine's grin.

The bills were crisp in his hands. Four twenties; three fives; four ones. Ninety-nine.

The bartender said, "A buck is off for me. Commission on the sale," and grinned.

Joe nodded, started for the door, but Pogie trotted beside him. "Hey, God damn it, Joe. Hey, aren't you going to buy a drink?"

Sure, that's what he was going to do. Joe Nighthawk was going to buy himself a celebration drink. He swung back to the counter, ordered a beer. He saw Pogie's look, and thought, "What the fuck!" and ordered one for him, too.

There were men on his left, behind him, with Pogie pushing closer, and Frenchy and Nick the Greek crowding in. It didn't seem right to ignore them.

Poor goddamn slobs, they hadn't won anything. "Buy for the house," Joe said grandly.

Later he walked carefully along the road. How many fucking rounds had he bought for the house? He didn't remember. He did recall fighting Pogie about the poker game, then Pogie's leaving in a trail of curses when Joe wouldn't listen. Joe wasn't sure how much he'd lost.

He felt in his shirt pocket. The citation! Motherfucking goddamn cop! And bills. Joe peered at them. Singles. Nine. Forty-seven cents' change. His wallet was empty. The hundred was as good as gone.

He sighed. It was good Geraldine didn't know about the win. She'd be mad at him for being so late. But that was nothing. If he could just get his face into her titties. Except, looking ahead, he saw lights in the house. The silhouette at the window. Pogie's truck at the front. Geraldine knew.

The stink of the fire in the yard blended with the stink of his breath. He was ready to turn tail and run.

Pogie came out, saw him. "Lose it all?"

"All but nine fucking dollars. And forty fucking seven cents."

"I tried to get Geraldine. She wouldn't come."

When Pogie had driven away, Joe went inside.

She looked at him. Forget the titties.

The silence lengthened. Finally he asked, "Why didn't you try to stop me?"

"I told Pogie you'd have sense enough to quit yourself."

"Only I didn't. And I lost damn near all of it." He choked out the rest. "And don't ask me why or how."

"I know how, and I guess I know why, too." She smiled suddenly. "So what? What difference would a hundred dollars make?"

"A full cupboard." Sickness came over him in a quick shocking wave. "Jesus, Mary, and Joseph! What the hell was I doing?"

She ignored the language. She put an arm around his shoulders. "I've still got the twenty-five. So we'll eat. Just the way we always have. You never let us go hungry, Joe."

The sickness went away as quickly as it had come. But he said, "That's not saying much."

"Only you had a pretty good time, didn't you? Now tell me the truth. Didn't you, Joe?"

He looked her in the eye, and grinned, and hugged her to him. "What I remember of it, I did."

At the other end of the cove, in the Landing Motel, Quinn pushed back her chair, and rose and stretched and rubbed her eyes. She had finished her paperwork. She was tired, ready for bed.

But the room was stuffy and stank of fresh paint from the hallways refurbished that day in preparation for the summer season yet to come.

She had forgotten the flat tire, the Indian who repaired it, and the tan sedan that had sped away when she parked the Rabbit.

She went to the window, pulled back the drapes, and glanced into the parking lot. Headlights glared at the corner where she had left the Rabbit for the night.

By morning the battery would be dead.

She dashed into the hall, ran for the closest stairwell. The fire door was heavy, but she jerked it open. As it closed silently behind her, she was engulfed in darkness. The overhead bulb was out.

But she knew the way. She had stayed at the motel many times before. She grasped the handrail firmly, took a first safe step, then a second. At the third, hurrying, with the battery on her mind, the drive to Saugatuck Island, she stepped forward.

Something struck her smartly at her shins. She fell forward, her grip on the railing broken. Even as she tumbled through black space, she heard a rattle and clatter, and along with it the quick shuffle of footsteps.

She fell hard on hands and knees, shaken and angry.

A Friend.

He'd been here with her. She'd even heard him hurry away.

She rose, stockings torn, both knees bloody. She limped into the parking lot and turned off the headlights.

The locked door of the Rabbit had probably been opened with the wire hanger that lay nearby.

Starting inside again, she ran into a maintenance man who had noticed the lights, he said, and was coming to check. Now he noticed her bloody knees, demanded to know what had happened.

He went with her to the stairwell. Sawhorses, a paint-stained board, lay on the landing where she had fallen. He flashed his light around once more, growled, "Damn lucky you didn't break your neck."

She agreed, went to her room.

Within moments the manager was knocking to ask if she was all right. He came with a first-aid kit. She sent him away. But soon he was back, this time with a doctor.

Ignoring her protests, the doctor checked her, announced her fit except for the cuts on her knees, which he cleaned with antiseptic and dressed with bandages.

When he had gone, she sighed with relief. But that was short-lived. The manager was back, form in hand.

"If you're really not hurt . . ." he said.

"I'm not."

"Then . . . this release . . ." As she signed it: "I've checked the bulb. I can't understand. It was only loosened. Probably some vibration from the highway. And I can tell you, some painters are going to be fired in the morning. Leaving that stuff in the stairwell . . . just imagine what could have happened . . ."

Alone.

She sank down on the edge of the bed, imagining what could have happened. The ambush. The dark. The hovering disaster.

Michael, she thought. The phone. It rang and rang and rang. She waited a long time. Finally she gave up and went to bed.

Morning. A bright day in May.

"Sure you're all right?" the desk clerk asked.

She nodded, paid her bill. She got into the Rabbit. She started a little before schedule for Saugatuck Island.

Three cars ahead of her, knowing her routine so well that he could lead instead of follow, Jerry saw the sun halo her bright hair.

She had gotten out of the Rabbit and looked right at him after giving the flat tire a disgusted inspection. He'd only meant to tease her a little. To remind her that he was around. But then that stinking old pickup had come up. He'd had to go on.

So there was that night . . .

She had come running down the steps toward him. He had seen her slender outline and waited, arms outstretched to receive her.

His Jenny. Jenny, who belonged to him and wanted him, and always had.

At the last moment, there was a yelp, a clatter. He remembered why he had loosened the light bulb, set up the board and sawhorses. Quinn Monroe. Lucky Quinn.

He fled from her to his room on the first floor. But she followed him. All through the night she moved in and out of his dreams. Quinn, who became Jenny, and lay lovingly in his arms . . .

When he turned into the Saugatuck Causeway, the Rabbit was only one car behind him.

CHAPTER 23

A heavy black storm cloud hung over Saugatuck Island, trailing the mutter of thunder over the ocean.

Serena Belton frowned at the wind-whipped trees in her yard. She hoped the rain would hold off until after her dinner guests arrived. She went into the living room.

Justin was frowning, too. But he was studying the stock market pages. It seemed to her that for the past three weeks every time she looked at him that was what he was doing.

"I hope Evelyn doesn't have trouble getting here," she said.

He threw the papers down, yelled, "How in the hell would I know if we're going to win!"

Openmouthed, silent, she stared at him, her small plump fists clenched at her sides. At last she managed a whispered "Justin, what *are* you talking about?"

"You know perfectly well—" A shamed grin flickered under his mustache. "Serena, what did you say to me?"

"I simply mentioned that I hope Evelyn doesn't have trouble getting here, and you—"

"I know. I guess it's on my mind."

She didn't ask him what was on his mind. She understood.

It had been that way since they'd won a place in the big bonus draw. Three weeks of waiting, of wondering. She had spent the $100,000 ten times in her imagination. She supposed he had, too.

"Only one more day to go," she murmured, smiling.

"I'll be glad when it's over."

"Me, too. And now I'd better go check the roast."

"It'll be perfect, as always."

Justin was right. The roast was just pink enough, and tender. The potatoes were smooth and creamy, the string beans crisp and green. The baked Alaska was a vast success.

The company of twelve was gay. But Serena, looking around the table, felt the weight of her leaden mood. No matter how she tried, the conversation kept returning to the lottery. What would she and Justin do with all that money?

"We might take a long trip," Justin said, a silly dreamy look on his face.

Serena sighed and kept silent. She didn't want to take a long trip. She didn't want to do anything but stay at home and enjoy her new kitchen and her friends.

"And I've been reading the stock market," Justin went on. "Though it doesn't seem a good time to invest."

Again Serena sighed and kept still. She considered the stock market a mysterious bore. And they already had enough money. What was this all about?

Evelyn, who was slim, bright-eyed, and huggable, laughed happily. "It's so exciting. I can hardly wait until tomorrow this time. Not every girl has a childless uncle and aunt who'll win that much money."

She was kidding, of course. Serena knew it, but she winced anyway.

And then Mary Carleton leaned toward Justin and made her dimples deepen. "I think a long trip would be the most adventurous thing to do."

Serena saw Justin straighten in his chair and smooth his mustache, preening as he said, "There's life in this old dog yet, you know."

Serena suddenly wished that she had gone to the beauty parlor that morning. She needn't be gray. She could have hair as golden as Mary Carleton's if she bothered. She could avoid potatoes and bread and slim herself down, too. And there was nothing that kept her from buying a new wardrobe. It was all within her power. She knew it. Yet . . . oh, it seemed too much trouble. She was middle-aged, a bit more even. Why did she have to pretend she wasn't?

There was a crack of thunder outside. She said brightly, "My, that sounded close, didn't it?"

Evelyn agreed. Then: "What time will you leave for St. Mary's City tomorrow?"

So they were back to the lottery again.

Serena refused to listen. She had heard it too many times in the past three weeks.

Wednesday. Justin came home from the shopping center, grinning. "Sit down, Serena. Leave those dishes alone. I've got something to tell you."

She obeyed. "You look about five years old."

"That's how I feel," he laughed. "Who'd imagine it possible?" Then, with a deep breath, "Listen, Serena, we've had the craziest thing happen to us."

She was instantly alarmed. "What's wrong?"

"You," he chuckled. "Always thinking of the worst first. Serena, we've won a place in the three-month bonus game. There'll be a draw in twenty-one days in St. Mary's City. We might have to be there, but I'm not sure."

"Oh, that's nice news. You had me worried for a minute."

"Serena, don't you understand?"

"You said we'd won—"

He cut in, "It's for a hundred thousand dollars."

"You're making it up to tease me because I've always made fun of your lottery tickets."

"Here. Look!" He thrust the paper at her.

She looked. *Justin Belton. Saugatuck Island, retired shoe manufacturer.*

She laughed. "My goodness, Justin. Your secret vice is going to pay off after all."

"I haven't won yet. There's still the draw, I told you."

"Oh, yes. That's right." She was breathless, shaky.

The phone rang. It continued to ring. That was the end of their quiet life.

She realized now, with a start, that the phone was ringing at that moment. Justin was half out of his chair.

She jumped up, trotted into the kitchen, calling back, "I'll get it."

It was Susan Brownlea, who lived down the road. "I want to wish you luck tomorrow, Serena. I'll be praying for you to win."

Thanking her, Serena thought, How odd for her to call. I haven't heard from her in weeks. And it was the same for the Cables, who had written to invite them to a cocktail party after a six-month silence. Of course Alan Cable had been ill for a long time, but just the same . . .

Serena returned to the table.

"Aunt Serena," Evelyn asked, "what are you going to wear tomorrow?"

"I hadn't thought."

"Oh, you must have some good-luck dress," Mary Carleton put in. "One that you always have fun in. That makes things go your way."

"I don't know," Serena murmured. She wished tomorrow were over with and done. She wished Mary Carleton looked her own age instead of ten years younger.

* * *

It was warm in St. Mary's City.

Dorsey had the window opened to its widest, hoping for a stray breeze as she stood before the mirror.

She had practiced a hundred times, a thousand times, readying herself for the opportunity when it came.

Tomorrow was the day.

So she practiced again. She reached into an imaginary bowl, plucked out a round disk. She sneezed violently, took a tissue from her pocket and wiped her nose, and thrust the used tissue into the other pocket. Between pluck and wipe, she substituted one small disk for another in a movement so smooth she herself didn't see how she had done it.

With a grin at her reflection, she turned away. She was as ready as she was ever going to be.

She crossed the room to where Bobsie slept in his too-small bed. If Henry Dalton had sent the support money, Bobsie would have a new one. He'd also be in a school where he could be taught to speak, and maybe a skill, so that he'd have a place in this world. He wouldn't be a cull for the rest of his life. He'd be Bobsie Dalton, who was maybe not quite like other people but still had the right to live and love.

But never mind Henry Dalton. What he hadn't been able to face, she had faced. Bobsie needed to win, and win he would.

Even after she divided the lottery money with Carrie, with the 20 percent taxes paid and the agent's commission, Dorsey knew she could still see Bobsie through his schooling. She'd miss him, but she'd manage somehow. Just as she'd managed to get herself into the position where she could make it possible.

The answer had come to her suddenly. She'd been busy at the typewriter. Ethel Johnson had sneezed. Dorsey saw the tissue in Ethel's hand, saw the papers fall from her fingers. It clicked then and there.

She knew she'd have to practice, but that was okay. It was easy to manage the disks because she helped number them. It was harder to get herself into the right place. She had never been asked to help at the drawing because everyone knew she wanted to be home with Bobsie after work. She overcame that hurdle by confiding to Ethel Johnson that always staying in got on her nerves, but she didn't want to date. After Henry Dalton the idea of trying to be nice to any man made her sick. So Ethel, the office gossip, spread the word. Someone finally suggested that Dorsey would be willing to work an occasional drawing.

Meanwhile Dorsey pretended to develop an allergy of noticeable proportion. She had sneezing fits that made her body convulse, and whatever she held flew from her fingers. She used tissue liberally. Soon the seizures were taken for granted.

Now she bent over Bobsie, kissed his round cheek. "I'd never do it for anything else. But it's for you. And that makes it okay."

It was a day later, and still warm in St. Mary's City.

The six-o'clock sun was high and bright. It glittered on silvered banners, and red-and-gold pennants, and the spangled uniforms of the combo that was playing the state anthem. The drums rolled; the guitar strummed; the trumpet blared.

Multicolored balloons drifted on glistening wire above the foot-high wood platform set in the middle of the parking lot. It was about the size of a boxing ring, and like a boxing ring, it was enclosed by ropes. At each of its four corners there stood a security guard.

In the ring's center, the master of ceremonies, plump, middle-aged, and bald, was setting up the audio system.

Dorsey, standing close by him, wore a pink sweater around her shoulders. Her skirt pocket was stuffed with tissue. Beneath them lay a blue disk stamped with the same number on the blue disk that represented Carrie Realin's ticket. Dorsey, as soon as she'd known Carrie's number was in the bonus draw, had managed, unobserved, to stamp the duplicate. Now it burned against her hip. She looked at the enormous glass globe that rested on a four-foot metal tripod. Within it, hundreds of different-colored disks were like a confetti collection.

She eyed them, waiting. A trickle of sweat ran down her back. She shrugged, sneezed, wiped her nose with tissue.

The M.C. suddenly boomed, "One, two, three. Testing," and the state anthem faded on a loud rumbling chord.

There was a rustle of anticipation in the crowds surging around the platform. The hopeful, the curious, the envious. They laughed and stared, always pressing closer to the ring. Children crawled between their legs, and tumbled over their feet, and dragged at their coats.

The participants wore carnations. Those in the bonus draw, the climax of the day's lottery, had red flowers. Contenders in the weekly had pink ones. The aspirants in the monthly draw were pinned with white. Ethel had given the flowers out as she checked the contenders in.

Dorsey caught Carrie Realin's eye, and waved, and received an excited salute in return. Dorsey smiled, sneezed into a tissue. Little did Carrie know . . .

The M.C.'s voice boomed, "Ladies and gentlemen, welcome to the state lotteries drawing. This evening we will have three of them. Some lucky people are going to go away happy. But you can all go away knowing that you've got a chance to win next time. Winners now and losers alike. Just remember there's always another chance. It *can* be your lucky day!"

He nodded at the combo. It swung into a hot version of "Somewhere over the Rainbow." The crowd cheered. Then there was "Happy Days Are Here Again."

Tension grew as the music faded.

Dorsey fingered the disk in her pocket, re-adjusted the tissue.

"And now," the M.C. said, laughing. "Now, what you've been waiting for." He turned dramatically toward Dorsey. "Here we have pretty Mrs. Dorsey Dalton, of the State Lottery Commission office, who will assist us this evening." And, as Ethel came to stand next to her, "Our Miss Ethel Johnson, who will help her." A long, significant pause. "Are we ready?"

The shouts went up. The combo began to play.

"Miss Johnson," the M.C. said. "The weekly, if you please."

She nodded, touched a switch. The huge glass globe turned slowly. The colored disks danced in random patterns.

"And now, Mrs. Dalton . . ."

Dorsey reached in, withdrew a red disk. As she brought it to the M.C., she sneezed into a tissue.

"And the winner in the weekly lottery is, for this particular week" —a long breathless moment—"Red 81 Green 02 Yellow 01." A moment's silence. Then: "Do I hear that number?" More silence. The M.C. shook his head sadly. "A pity to miss the excitement." He consulted a card. "Mr. Jerry Tolan is the winner of a fifty-two-foot mobile home. And he'll receive it, even though he isn't with us today."

Serena Belton clung to Justin's arm, shivering uncontrollably.

The roll of drums. The trumpets' blare. Dorsey made the draw. There was an announcement by the M.C. A heavy-set woman flung herself against the ropes, screaming, "It's me! Me!" She had won four thousand dollars in the monthly draw.

The fanfare of trumpets. The roll of drums. "And now, ladies and gentlemen, the cherry on the whipped cream! The moment we've all been waiting for. The one-hundred-thousand-dollar bonus draw! Mrs. Dalton, if you please."

The shining glass bowl turned slowly. The disks spun and bounced and danced. Dorsey reached in, seized one, and withdrew her hand. She sneezed loudly, quickly pulled tissue from her pocket. In a smooth swift movement she dropped the disk from the bowl into the tissue. She sneezed twice again as she went to the M.C. By then, the disk she had stamped with Carrie's number was in her hand, while the tissue and the disk from the bowl were safely back in her pocket. The substitution was done. Later, when the bowl was returned to the office, she would find Carrie's original disk among all the others and destroy it.

The M.C. read off the number. Carrie Realin gave a shrill cry of joy, then burst into happy sobs, and allowed the M.C. to lead her into the ring, where the young photographer took pictures of her for the *Lottery Commission News,* and Dorsey smiled pleasantly, clasping the tissue in her pocket where the disk with Justin Belton's number was hidden.

He knew nothing of that, however. His tense body went slack. He bent his head. "It's over, Serena."

She raised her eyes to his, breath held.

He smiled ruefully. "There goes our long trip."

"We didn't win?"

"No."

She let her breath out. She found herself laughing, though there were tears in her eyes. "I was woolgathering. Oh, Justin, I'm so sorry. But I'm glad."

He hugged her.

"You're not mad at me?"

"No. And let's go home and drink up the champagne."

"You're really not disappointed?" she asked, when they were on the way back to Saugatuck Island.

"Too much happening for us anyhow," he answered. "We were changing. Peculiar things coming into our heads."

"You can stop reading the stock market pages."

"And you can stop wondering why people invite you to their parties."

"Let's call Evelyn and tell her it's okay."

"She'll know that. Let's call her to say hello."

They were silent for a few minutes, and then Serena said, "Did you notice the face of the girl that won? How astounded and happy she was? And what she said she'd do? Build a big house and take care of brain-damaged children?"

Justin nodded soberly. "It was good." Then: "Serena, do you mind if I stop at the liquor store? We're low on gin."

"You want to get a ticket," she said, grinning.

"My secret vice," he answered, signaling for a turn into the shopping center.

That evening the St. Mary's City *News* had a picture of Carrie Realin, the stunned winner of $100,000, in the state lottery's bonus draw.

Next to it, a headline read NO INDICTMENT. The first paragraph stated that Adelaide Herman, April winner of a $70,000 prize in the state lottery, had been cleared of all charges in the shooting death of her husband, George Herman, prominent St. Mary's City developer, who had died six weeks before, having beaten his wife and struggled with her for the gun by which he was shot. Mrs. Herman, still prostrated by shock, the item went on, refused to speak to reporters.

The sun had set, leaving thin trails of fading pink in the sky over Riverton.

Molly said, "It's changed my life, Mary. You should've seen the man's face. I worked for him three years, and he never noticed me. Always blank-eyed and grouchy. Today he stares, says I look different. So I told him about Becker's."

"I'm glad the new way we tried it last night worked," Mary said. "You doing okay?"

Mary nodded. "And maybe I'll have another demonstration party soon."

"It's no good. Waiting for the women to come to you. If you went to them—"

"I couldn't. Knocking on doors—"

"In the park. Oh, come on. They're your friends. Even the ones you don't know yet. Just do it around noon. Go for a visit, a quickie. Try it and you'll see."

"I couldn't," Mary repeated. And, faintly: "I'm scared of the dogs."

"That's why they bark at you."

"Gus always says the same." Pause. "Said."

Molly got up. "Come on. I'll show you how to take care of dogs. Have dinner with us tonight. And on the way I'll prove my system to you."

"But I can't. Really."

Molly said, "I'm just going to show you. I won't let you get bitten. And besides, having a meal with me won't kill you. I'm a pretty good cook."

So Mary went with Molly. They walked down the road together. The barking began near the tall pines. Mary froze.

But Molly took her hand. "Now watch."

The two dogs raced out, baying in full throat.

"Why, you dumb-ass sons of bitches," Molly said in a sweet and loving tone, "you come a step nearer to us, you mothers, and I'll tear you tails off and shove them straight up your assholes." Gently, the words rolled from her smiling lips. "You fuckers, get back and sit down and leave us alone," she crooned.

Still speaking, she went on, drawing Mary with her, as the dogs' yowls softened to yips and then faded, and they trotted docilely alongside the two women until they turned in to Molly's trailer.

"You see?" Molly asked.

Mary nodded, giggled. "Dumb-ass sons of bitches won't bother me anymore."

Later, working on the accounts sheets Quinn had given her: Delivered. Paid for. They were even to the penny. Not such a lot. Next week there'd be more. Even more after that. But never $50,000. Only she'd never had the $50,000 so she hadn't lost it. Gus. She felt a quick clench at her heart. But Gus was gone. And she was making it. Making it on her own. Mary Easter was okay.

When she heard the yowls outside, she raised her head to listen. She giggled. Dumb-ass dogs.

CHAPTER 24

Jerry lay in bed, remembering.

There had been a night. A shaggy-limbed tree. Ears ringing, breathless from volcanic eruption, he had fled from what he'd seen, from pursuit, too.

He'd found his bed and hid there, clothes bunched and wrinkled and smelling of pine needles and sweat and semen. He never knew how long he had been there. He'd seen the light at the window, and dark, in succeeding patterns. He'd heard traffic hum on the Old North Road, and heard it fade away to periods of silence in succeeding rhythms, too.

Time had passed. He knew that the toilet down the hall had been flushed, the tub had been filled and emptied. Footsteps had whispered slowly past his door.

He'd ignored time and sound, and stared at the living images that moved on the ceiling above his staring eyes.

The thresh of silken legs . . . the thrust of narrow hips . . . the spill of hair along a pillow . . . a swift stroking tongue and mouth that suckled . . . and she went astride all flowing movement . . .

He, watching: seized, squeezed, drained. And then the flight into the dark.

Wanton. That was what he had thought. Wanton. Wicked. And there would always be men for her. Men. But not him.

The transistor whispered close by. Music faded. Then: "The season's strong upon us. King's has all you need for that secluded weekend in the wilds. Shop King's for all your camping supplies."

Without his knowing it, the words registered. He was back then, when it had happened. The moving images faded into new ones. Short chestnut curls. Dreaming eyes fixed on the light that spilled in at the end of the dark culvert . . . a small slick body, tomboy muscles hard with sinew. The mound curved and hairless, and within it, the pink tip that turned cherry-red when he touched it . . .

His body had shaken, seized in a giant fist, was squeezed, emptied of breath. His ears had rung with a dull distant chiming of heated and pounding blood. Adrift in agonized pleasure, his blinded eyes had sought the disappearing images. He fell into blackness.

A knocking had roused him. Mrs. Varnick's voice. "Mr. Lakes?

Jimmy? Are you all right? It's been three days now. Can I get you something?"

"I'm okay." He had croaked it from a parched throat. His pants were wet, cold. He was weak and despairing of knowing strength again. "I'm okay." Had it been three days? Was that how long it had been?

"But I'd be so glad—"

"Just resting. I'll see you later," he'd said.

Her footsteps pattered away.

He sank back. He had remembered.

Wanton. She would always have men. But she belonged to him.

"No, Jerry. I'm not going to the culvert anymore."

"Jerry! What are you doing here? Why are you following me around?"

"Jerry, if you don't leave me alone—"

"Jerry, don't you know I want you? But it's wrong! Wrong!"

She belonged to him, and always had, and always would.

He had licked his parched lips, waiting.

It would come. He would know what to do. He had only to wait.

But he hadn't waited. He'd followed her to Saugatuck Island, and she had come toward him through the night.

Now he lay abed again, remembering . . .

The transistor whispered, "No one, can you believe it, folks? No one guessed the name of the ninety-one-year-old man once known as the Hermit of New England. So two tickets to *Taxi Driver*, now playing at the *Atheneum* in St. Mary's City, are up for grabs."

St. Mary's City . . . Adelaide Herman. The blonde who had everything, and luck, too. And Riverton, where pretty Mary Baker lived in a trailer park. And there had been something in Windsor, too . . .

He brushed the errant thoughts away. No. They didn't matter now. Not yet. First there was something . . .

Two hours later, he saw it all. The answer had flowered in his mind. He had it in every detail. It was necessary for him only to follow through. Clearly, without knowing it, he'd been making his preparations for a long time.

He rose, went downstairs.

Mrs. Varnick caught up with him at the front door. "Oh, Mr. Lakes, are you going out?"

"Yes."

"I'm so glad. Ever since that last time, when you stayed in bed so long—"

"I'm fine."

"If you'd want me to fix you some dinner—"

"I'll eat out. I have to go to Passamody."

The sun was high and warm. The front yard was green with foot-tall weeds.

"She belongs to me," he said aloud, as he pulled into the Old North Road.

Later that day, Mrs. Varnick smiled at May, the cashier in Fieldstone's. "Oh, I'm so relieved. It's all right. He's up and around. After that last time he stayed in bed so long I got worried. I didn't know what to do. But he's fine, he said."

That night May told her sister Eva, "That poor old woman's going dotty. She broods over her roomer the way a hen broods on an egg," and when Eva mentioned it to her husband Lacy Pickett, he said, "She's got to have someone, I guess. It might as well be him."

In Passamody, Jerry took his time. No need to hurry. Camp beds and two sets of red draperies in King's. Red was her favorite color. He bought canned goods in Riverton and thought of Mary Baker again, but decided to wait. When the tan sedan was loaded, he drove back to Elkhorn.

There was time.

He would continue the next day.

CHAPTER 25

In Boston, Michael drove straight to the *Globe*. He traveled streets he had driven with Katherine, passing restaurants where they had eaten together. He didn't think of her with anger or regret. Her name simply crossed his mind.

In the morgue, the newspaper library, a young black man was glad to allow Michael to go into the files, while he himself checked the catalog.

Finally he said, "Nope. Sorry, Mr. Dayman. No Kenyon, Kansas. I guess nothing's ever happened there."

"Let's try Lakas then. Jenny Lakas."

In a little while the young man said, "Nothing."

With his permission, Michael put in a call to a friend on *The New York Times*, asked the same questions, gave his number. The return call came within the hour. The *Times* had mentioned Kenyon, Kansas, once. A single paragraph stating that a new east-west bypass had turned the once thriving railhead into a ghost town. Jenny Lakas was mentioned once, too. Another single paragraph, stating that she had died by suicide in a jump from the balcony of a Chevy Chase, Maryland, apartment house.

Nothing new to Michael. He remembered that Steve Gregson, a former colleague, had come from Kansas City. But Steve wasn't in the city room. It took Michael another hour to locate him in a delicatessen three blocks from the office.

Steve blinked up at him over a beer. "Am I seeing things? Or have you come back?"

Michael sat down, shook his head, ordered a beer when the waitress came. "I need a favor, Steve."

"I'm broke, Michael. The wife spends it faster than I can earn it. VISA's breathing down our necks."

"Not money. Information. Aren't you from Kansas City?"

"A town *near* there."

"Have you ever heard of Kenyon, Kansas?"

Steve groaned. "A nothing place."

"You have contacts in the town?"

"Nobody to have contacts with. Last time I went through it was blowing away in the wind."

"No newspaper? Wire service stringers?"

Steve shook his head. "You'd have to see it to understand. Even the sheriff's gone. He retired three years ago. They never got another. I guess somebody from the state highway patrol stops there for a cup of coffee once a year."

"What about in Kansas City, Steve? Anybody you could call for me? I need to know about a family in Kenyon."

Steve studied Michael suspiciously. "That's all you want?"

"Just find out if there's a Lakas family in Kenyon. L A K A S. If there was a daughter named Jenny. What other relatives there are. And where they are now."

"What's it about?"

"Nothing you'd be interested in."

Steve said Michael was up to something, but okay, he'd make the call. They went back to the phone booth. Michael supplied the change.

It was another hour before Steve made contact. He asked his questions, got a promise of a return call. In forty minutes, he was on the phone again. Michael waited at his shoulder.

Steve repeated what he heard. "Jenny Lakas . . . from an old obit in the *Star*. Okay. What? August 1977, died suddenly in Washington, D.C., returned for burial to her home, Kenyon, Kansas. Survived by her parents Mortimer and Elvira Lakas, and one brother Jerry."

"Hold it," Michael said excitedly. "Ask where the brother is now. Have him call Kenyon, if he has to."

"There's nothing to call in Kenyon," Steve answered. "I told you." Then, into the phone: "This Jerry guy—" Steve paused because Michael was poking him, saying, "I want everything about the brother. Where he is now. His age. What he drives. It's important, Steve."

No time now to let himself think how important. But Quinn flashed through his mind.

Steve repeated the questions into the phone. And: "I know you can't. But wait, I'll put him on. His name is Dayman. The Pulitzer-prize Dayman, for Christ's sake. I don't know what it's about."

Michael took the phone. "Thanks for helping. It's urgent." He gave his number in Elkhorn, his address. "And if you can get a picture of him, any kind, the faster the better . . ."

After he'd hung up, he said, "I'll buy you another beer before I leave." And: "Your friend's reliable, isn't he?"

"He won't forget about it. I'll bet you ten that you hear from him inside of two days. And have a picture, if one's available, inside of a week. If the Postal Service plays ball."

"You're on," Michael grinned.

Two days later, he mailed Steve a ten-dollar bill.

The call from Kansas City had come through that night. Jenny's surviving brother, Jerry Lakas, was thirty-three years old. He'd left Kenyon in late February or early March, and had not been back since. He owned a tan Oldsmobile, probably a 1975 or 1976 model. He was unmarried, had no known friends, worked in his father's drugstore, was considered a loner, was believed to have disappeared before and returned after some time.

"What about Jenny?"

"My source only knew that she went away to teacher's college and never stayed home anymore. It was years ago. There was some talk at church, but the family kept mum."

"What kind of talk?"

"Like was she pregnant and unmarried. Or was she a dope fiend."

"And the picture?"

"It's on the way. A clip of a poor high school graduation yearbook photo. The best I could do."

Michael thanked his caller, hung up.

He consulted his watch. Four P.M. Too early to phone Quinn in Saugatuck Island. But it was 3 P.M. in Kenyon, Kansas. He dialed for Kansas Information, got Topeka, Topeka referred him on to Kansas City, Kansas. Within moments, he had two Lakas numbers in Kenyon. One home. One drugstore.

He considered. Sometimes a woman was easier to bully. If it was necessary. A woman of Elvira Lakas's age. He called himself a son of a bitch, said "Quinn" in his mind, dialed the home number.

A single ring. A woman's voice, tentative, breathy, "Hello?" A question in the acknowledgment.

He introduced himself by name only, went on. "I'm trying to locate your son Jerry, Mrs. Lakas. Can you tell me where he is?"

There was a gasp. A heartbeat of silence. Then: "I'm sure he'll be home soon. He loves the spring here. The lilacs in the yard . . . I know he'll come back?" With that question again. That hope.

Michael wished he hadn't called her. He said hoarsely, "Thanks, Mrs. Lakas."

Quickly, before he could change his mind, he called the drugstore number.

"Lakas Pharmacy. Good afternoon." An elderly voice. False briskness covering bone-deep fatigue.

A fleeting memory of Nathaniel Gordon touched Michael, was gone.

He gave his name again, said, "Mr. Lakas, I'd like to find your son Jerry. Do you happen to know where he is?"

"Dayman? I don't know you from Adam." Cautious. Thoughtful.

"I realize that. But it's urgent."

"What's urgent?" Suspicious now. Fearful, too?

"That I talk to him."

A silence. Then: "I don't know where Jerry Lakas is. And I don't care. I used to have a son by that name. But not anymore. If you ever find him, tell him I said so." A click.

Michael listened to the hum of the wire. But the man *did* care. There had been clear pain in that elderly voice . . .

Later that evening he telephoned Quinn. Her room didn't answer. When he tried the next morning she had already checked out. It bothered him that he had missed her. He knew she'd be leaving Saugatuck Island, heading south toward Elkhorn, with a few stops along the way. But he wouldn't be able to reach her now until she arrived home.

The mail came at ten o'clock. And with it the picture of Jerry Lakas. It was, as Michael had been warned, blurred. The young face that looked at him from the thin paper was nondescript and unfamiliar. It had an old-fashioned hairstyle, a two-inch brush cut that made the ears stand out from the head. It had deep-set dreamy eyes. A sensitive mouth.

Michael put it carefully into its envelope and set out through the heavy Friday-morning traffic.

He made his first stop at the garage. Bill Sears studied the photograph carefully, then shook his head. "No, Mike. He doesn't ring a bell."

"Try to imagine him about fifteen years older, say, at thirty-three."

Bill shrugged. "Doesn't help none."

It was the same at Fieldstone's, at Cory's Wine and Liquor, at the Burger Barn.

Michael began to wonder if he were wasting his time. Maybe he was all wrong. Jerry Lakas had left home, but not to come to Elkhorn.

But he kept going, even including a stop at the Rolls-Royce dealership across the road from Mrs. Varnick's house.

When he'd covered every place in the town that he could think of he decided to go to see Lacy Pickett at the State Police substation. With the old picture, and the description of the car, Lacy could check for Jerry Lakas's presence anywhere in the state.

But it was afternoon by then, and when Michael reached Old Barn Road he slowed, turned in. He'd stop and see if Quinn was home yet. He was anxious to tell her what he knew about Jerry, and certain that once he had, she could contribute enough about what had happened in Washington to enable Michael to get a fix on Jerry as intuition said he must, or else to dismiss Jerry as a false trail, and begin anew.

But the Rabbit wasn't parked in the yard.

He stopped only because Helen came out.

She leaned at the open window. "I thought you were Quinn."

"She should be here soon. Tell her I'll be back in a little while."

"But she *was* here," Helen said.

"What?"

"Several hours ago, Michael. She whipped in, and unloaded, and changed and whipped out. An appointment in Passamody to interview the new district manager that Becker's is sending in."

"She never mentioned that before." Uneasy. Somehow doubtful.

"It just came up. They called her from the central office yesterday."

"When's she coming back?"

"It should be now. She grabbed the shopping list, said she'd do it on the way, and to tell you to plan dinner here tonight."

"Okay." He reached for the ignition. There was something about Helen's face that stopped the gesture. "What's wrong?"

"Her knees were bandaged, Michael. When I asked what happened, she pretended she hadn't heard me."

He hadn't been able to get her the night before; this morning she had checked out. Bandaged knees.

He and Helen both turned to look down Old Barn Road at the same time. No apple-green Rabbit.

"I'll wait here," he said, and got out of the car.

Inside the house, he showed Helen the photograph of Jerry Lakas. "Have you seen this man around here? Imagine him about fifteen years older, if you can."

She frowned at the picture. "Who is it?"

"Jerry Lakas."

"A relative of Jenny's?" Helen gasped.

Michael nodded. "I think he might be Quinn's letter writer. And he's not at home where he belongs. So he could have come here."

Helen studied Jerry's young face for a long silent moment. "I don't know . . . but somehow there's something familiar about him." She drew a ragged breath. "It's just a feeling. But maybe I've seen him."

No one else who'd seen the picture had said that, yet Michael felt less uncertain now. That Jerry would have found some pretext for coming to Helen's door seemed reasonable. That her artist's eye might retain a faint memory of a faint resemblance seemed just as reasonable.

Michael waited out a half an hour, pacing. Then he said, "I'm going down to Fieldstone's. Maybe she's stuck in the Friday shopping rush."

He jounced too fast into the ruts of Old Barn Road, skidded wildly at the curve, and jammed on his brakes in the shadow of the new-budded birch trees.

The Rabbit was before him, half on the road, half on the narrow rock shoulder.

Its door hung open.

He jumped out of his car, yelled, "Quinn! Where are you?"

A truck rumbled on the Old Barn Road. A bird trilled.

Shouting her name again, he went to the Rabbit. It was empty. A single lemon lay on the front seat. A crumpled travel folder. He picked it up. Kashmir.

When he closed the car door, a silver button fell at his feet.

He never remembered what happened in the next few minutes. Suddenly he was at the house. Helen was saying, "The car's there and she's gone? But that's crazy, Michael!"

"Get me Becker's central office number, quick," he said. "Let's make sure of the appointment in Passamody."

Within moments he knew that Quinn had met a woman named Stacy Deward at the Passamody Hotel, at three o'clock, and at three forty-five, she had called personnel at Becker's to recommend her for the job.

"Call the State Police," Helen said.

"I'm going there." Michael jerked the door open. "Phone me if you hear from her."

Again he jounced too fast into the ruts of Old Barn Road. Planning what he would tell Lacy Pickett.

But at Sears' garage, he stopped to ask if anyone had noticed the Rabbit go by, and if so, when.

"Yep. Saw her about an hour ago," Bill Sears said. "She waved at me." Then: "Why?"

Michael explained about the car.

Bill tossed the station keys to an employee. "I'll be back later." And to Michael: "Let's go see Lacy."

It took only moments to drive to the State Police substation. But Lacy Pickett was busy.

Mrs. Varnick was saying, "You ought to be able to tell me what to do, Lacy."

"There's nothing to do," the blond trooper told her. "If he's been gone a few days and didn't say he was leaving, then just pack up his stuff and save it for him."

"He took it all," she said. "I looked."

The trooper smiled at her patiently. "Go ahead and rent your room again. As long as he doesn't owe you money, there's nothing to worry about."

"But he didn't say goodbye," she said sadly.

Michael cleared his throat.

Bill Sears shuffled his big feet.

"Funny, the way he was accumulating," she muttered. "Canned goods and blankets." She pushed herself out of her chair, nodded at Michael and Bill as she passed them.

Michael turned immediately to the state trooper. "Lacy, something's happened to Quinn. She's disappeared. I just found her car on Old Barn—" His voice faded. Then: "Who was Mrs. Varnick talking about?"

"Some guy named Lakes that rented from her. He took off a couple of days ago, and hasn't come back."

"Lakes. Took off a couple of days ago. Accumulating . . ."

Michael raced out, caught up with Mrs. Varnick, persuaded her to return to the substation.

Inside she looked reproachfully at Lacy. "You never told me what to do about Mr. Lakes."

"That's the right name?" Michael demanded. "You're sure?"

"I ought to know my own roomer's name."

"He didn't say he was leaving?" Lacy asked.

"No."

"When did he go?"

"Two or three days ago. I'm not absolutely certain. He wasn't feeling so good for a while. Some time back he stayed in bed three whole days and I never even saw or heard him. Then one day he got up, and after that he was in and out. So I was never sure if he was at home. And I saw"—here wrinkled cheeks turned pink—"one night I just happened to notice that he had his car—"

Michael: "What kind of car, Mrs. Varnick?"

"Tan. Old. I don't know anything else about cars. But he had a lot of stuff in it. And I was worried he'd cook in his room. And then, today, I realized he was gone."

"You don't remember the car license plate?" Lacy put in.

"Me? License plate?"

"When did he come?" Michael.

"Let me think." An agonizingly long pause. Then: "In March. But I don't recall exactly. In the middle of the month, I guess."

"His checks were on what bank?" That was Lacy again.

"He paid in real money, Lacy. You know how hard it is for me to get around to cash checks."

Lacy turned to the telephone. Within a few minutes he had the license number and registration of the plates on the tan car, under the name of Jerry Lakas.

Mrs. Varnick looked astonished. "I could have sworn it was Jimmy Lakes."

Michael said, "One more question, Mrs. Varnick. Did he ever mention a favorite place of his? Or where he was going from here?"

"My goodness, that man, he just drove all over St. Mary's City. Jewell's Landing. Saugatuck Island. It was helping him get well, he told me."

When she had gone, Lacy said, "Okay. We'll get out an all-points on this car. Although there's no real grounds, Mike."

"Quinn's gone," Michael said.

"Only for a few hours. If that. She could have left her car, gone off with a friend. You'd better cool down and get ready to wait awhile."

Michael said evenly, "When you've made your call, I want you to listen to me."

Lacy shrugged. With the bulletin out, he turned back to Michael, nodded from time to time at the picture Michael drew for him.

It began with Jenny's suicide. Michael admitted he didn't know the why of that, or its connection with Quinn. He was only certain there was one. Quinn came to Elkhorn, lived quietly and without being troubled until she won the lottery.

Wincing at the memory of how he had suggested that she buy the ticket in the first place, he went on to describe what had happened after.

The letters from *A Friend* that had frightened her, but that Lacy had dismissed. The whole series of things that had been laid at the door of coincidence.

Here Bill Sears grunted. "Slashed tires."

Michael went on. The slaughtered cat that had finally led Michael to see that Quinn was in danger. Her obdurate refusal to discuss Jenny Lakas after the Peeping Tom had finally forced the girl's name from Quinn's lips.

The realization that Kenyon, Kansas, where Jenny was from, and Kansas City, Missouri, where the letters had been mailed, were so close together.

Jerry, and the discovery that he had left home in early March, or late February, and hadn't been seen there since.

When Michael finished, Bill Sears said, "You see it, don't you, Lacy?"

But the trooper replied, "All conjecture. But I'll admit it's convincing. And I agree it's something to work with. But Jerry Lakas could have gone anywhere in the world, for a million reasons you don't know about. And by now you might find Quinn at home."

"She didn't go off and leave the car door open." Michael pulled the silver button from his pocket. "And I found this when I slammed the door. I think she left it there on purpose."

"It's possible." Lacy sounded doubtful. Then: "We'll wait another hour or so. I'll start asking around, and get some help on it. You two do the same, why don't you? Let's see if we can turn her up somewhere around Elkhorn before we push the panic button."

Michael and Bill drove up and down the Old North Road.

Quinn had been in Cory's Wine and Liquor Store. She had done the usual weekend shopping at Fieldstone's. What the hell had happened to the groceries? he asked Bill. There'd been only the lemon left in the car. Michael didn't mention the crumpled Kashmir pamphlet. Bill Sears recalled again that she'd waved as she drove past his garage.

After that they found no trace of her. She had stopped the Rabbit on Old Barn Road, and gotten out, and disappeared.

When the two men returned to the State Police substation, Lacy said, "We've got the car. It was on a used-car lot up in Ballston. Turned in for four hundred dollars cash, three days ago. By Jerry Lakas."

"What did he get in return? He must have bought another car."

"Not there. And he didn't get a new registration in that name either. At least not in this state."

"Try Massachusetts," Bill said.

"It's in the works."

Michael and Bill went back to the house.

Michael didn't have to ask. Helen was red-eyed, shaking.

Quinn was still gone.

CHAPTER 26

Quinn slowed the Rabbit as she bumped into the start of the deep curve. Good that there would be someone ready to take her place in Becker's line-up. One less thing to think about. Time was growing short. Michael. It wouldn't be easy. But she had to. *Had* to. Maybe later . . . somehow . . .

With a jolt, she slammed on her brakes. The car swerved half off the lane onto the stony edge.

She muttered angrily. An unfamiliar black automobile was blocking the way, its hood and trunk both raised.

Somebody *would* get stuck there. And when she had a load of frozen food. She'd have to walk the few hundred yards to the house, which was probably where the driver of the abandoned car was, trying to get Bill Sears on the phone. Helen would help her carry the bags back.

Quinn tucked her purse under her arm, swung the door open.

A man came out of the stand of birches. He walked toward her, smiling.

In the moment or two before he reached her, it crossed her mind that he'd stopped to relieve himself and must be embarrassed to see her here. For that reason, she wasn't afraid.

He wore wire-rimmed glasses on which the light glinted, and had longish chestnut hair. A lightweight blue jacket. Tan trousers. Somehow slightly familiar. Someone she'd seen around Elkhorn, she guessed.

He said, "Hi, I'm sorry I'm in the way."

Too late, alarm swept her. Why, exactly, she didn't know. But something. Something.

She reached out to close the Rabbit's door.

"Wait," he said. Voice rough with passion. Eyes burning. "Wait, Jenny! Don't run away anymore."

"Jenny?" The past suddenly alive on a late Friday afternoon. The beginning of sunset. On the horizon a drift of thick clouds. *"Jenny?"*

Her pained questioning whisper was cut off abruptly.

His hand was over her mouth. He jerked her forward against the half-open door, then out into the lane.

A moment of fierce struggle. A tangle of arms, legs. Fists. Clawed hands. Harsh breaths. A silenced scream in her throat. Swift and explosive pain in her head. Then dullish twilight—a half darkness in which she floated, numbed but conscious.

A pretense of complete unawareness to avoid another blow. At any cost, she must know what was happening.

Ambush.

Michael, Michael . . .

She was dragged, heels loose, scuffing her shoes, along the lane, and then lifted by an arm that encircled her waist.

Fight now? No. Impossible to win.

She kept her eyes closed, breathed deeply.

Something jammed into her mouth and forced the scream back before it was begun. She let her head roll limply. A binding over the gag, knotted on her neck. A gentle stroke against her hair? What?

The fall was sudden, sickening. Pain thudded at her temples, her bandaged knees. Her ankle and leg were twisted. Her body was turned, adjusted. The hem of her skirt pulled down. Jacket collar straightened. Again, What? A slam that rocked her from head to toe. *Jenny*.

She sucked air into her nose, breathing hard now. She opened her eyes to look. Dark. Cramped. The trunk of the car. Hood opened to make her think there was engine trouble. Trunk open to receive her.

Who was he? But she knew. *A Friend*. She'd been waiting for him for a long time.

Another slam. The hood was down. The motor hummed. Tires spun back gravel.

They were moving now. But where? Why?

Jenny.

He *had* said Jenny's name, hadn't he?

She twisted her head. It caught on something, and her hair snagged. She wriggled an arm free, worked her fingers to loosen the caught curl. The double knot at her neck pressed bruisingly. She plucked at it, imagining the gag pulled out, her screams.

No good. It would take two hands. She tried but couldn't manage it. But her position had been changed with the small movements she'd made.

Now she saw the faintest glimmer of light. Where did it come from in this enclosed place? Maybe a badly fitted joint in the trunk lid. She tried. Her exploring hand found no opening.

As she wriggled again, her knee jammed into metal that protruded beyond the trunk itself. There was a draft on her shin below the edge of the bandages put on at Jewell's Landing. No time to think of that. It took some doing, but when she had readjusted herself she could see the gleam of light more clearly. It came through where the bumper brace was set into the chassis.

She felt her purse against her foot, but there was no way to reach it. Stretching, straining, her searching fingers couldn't grasp it. Bits and pieces within it. If she could get at them . . . a tiny trail perhaps. But no.

As she drew her hand toward her, it brushed a frazzle of torn threads. She explored. One of her silver buttons was gone. Helen had noticed it, offered to sew it back on tighter. Quinn had said she'd do it herself, forgotten. Helen—she'd expect Quinn home by now. Michael—invited to dinner. What would they do? How long would they wait before they began to wonder about her? She'd always come, gone as she pleased. It would be a long time.

No. Not Michael. He'd remember the Peeping Tom. He'd remember his questions. He wouldn't wait.

But how did she know? She *knew*.

The button. Her fingers paused at the frazzle of threads. Why, of course. She ripped the next one loose, the other after.

Straining again, she found the bumper brace, felt the draft on the fingers, and dropped the button into the opening.

She heard a rhythmic rattle, sighed.

It was stuck. It wouldn't fall to the road. The car bounced. She listened again. That time the rattle was gone.

Encouraged, she slipped a second button into the opening at the brace.

The car slowed, stopped. A truck rumbled by. The Old North Road. A left turn. They'd soon be passing the place where she had skidded at the JESUS SAVES sign. Then Sears' garage and Fieldstone's . . .

She worked another button free, clutched it in sweating fingers. They were going fast now.

But where? Why? A quick trail of memories . . . Devil. The Rabbit squatting on ripped tires. Ribbons of what remained of her clothes. *Do you know how lucky you are?* And: *Are you enjoying your good fortune? To be lucky and ALIVE?*

No! She refused the memories. She clutched the buttons in a

sweaty fist, imagining those that were left on Old Barn Road. One lost. One deliberately left there.

Michael would see them, know.

But how could he? The loose gravel . . . He *would* see them, she told herself. And the Rabbit, the groceries. He would know.

Two more buttons. But she held them.

Where were they going, she and *A Friend?*

What was happening?

Who was the man who had called her Jenny, who had said, "Don't run away anymore?" Stroked her hair, adjusted her collar. Had Jenny run from him to her death?

Why had he called her, Quinn, by Jenny's name?

She rolled slightly as the car turned left again. Her head jerked on her shoulders, banged on metal. Dizziness swept her. She fought it off. She must be watchful, even if she couldn't see. She must be fully alert when he stopped. She clutched the last two silver buttons tightly.

A slow jostling drive now. The rattle of stones. Beyond that, silence. Silence. Where were they? There might have been another turn somewhere along the way, but she wasn't sure.

The car stopped. She quickly dropped a silver button into the brace opening. She hoped it wasn't wasted. It made a tinkling sound as the trunk lid snapped open.

"Jenny?" A worried whisper. "You all right?"

She opened her eyes to dim light. A silhouette bent near her. Beyond its shoulders, an opening to the sky and a tangle of thick vines.

"Jenny, please. I didn't mean to hurt you. I didn't hurt you, did I?"

She frowned, moved her head slightly.

"You're all right, aren't you?"

She managed to get her hand to her mouth, indicating the gag.

"I can't," he said. "Not just yet. But I will in a minute. I promise. Only you'll have to promise, too. Will you be good? Cross your heart and hope to die?" At her nod, he went on, "You'll come with me?" She nodded again.

But her eyes were wide, dark with fear. The pale freckles stood out on her face like small splashes of ink.

He took her hand in his, slipped an arm around her, lifted her out of the trunk.

"Don't be scared," he was saying. "It's only your own Jerry. You don't have to be scared of me."

But even as he spoke, he forced both her hands together in a crushing grip and bound them. That done he said, "It's not that I don't trust you, Jenny. But I've got to be sure. Now we'll go in, and it'll be all right."

He moved with her held tightly to him, clutching her bound hands.

The car was in a shed of some kind. They went from dimness through tangled vines into fading sunset.

She saw a rusted pump. The house that had once belonged to Helen's family. The hill and greening meadows broken by a line of trees. Far below, there was the roof of what used to be an old barn on Old Barn Road.

So close. But who would know?

Michael . . .

Jerry said thickly, "Just the two of us, Jenny. And safe. All boarded up. No way in. No way out. You'll like it, Jenny."

She could have flung herself to the ground near the pump. She could have flung herself away, trying to run.

She did neither.

She went with him willingly, in a fever to know.

Jenny. Eventually he would explain about Jenny.

She need wait only a little longer. She dropped the last of the buttons.

He was pleased. He stroked her hair back from her face, smoothed it over her ears.

He looked long and carefully down the hill and across the meadows. There was nothing. No stir of movement.

But as he led her toward the house, he jerked to a stop. A white cat stalked a leaf. He glared at it, but said, "We go around here, you see. This side," and led her to where the wing doors to the cellar lay flat against the earth, invisible with their mat of rotted lilac leaves. He ripped a live flowered limb from the bush. "Always hated these goddamn things."

She slanted her eyes at the white cat. Snowball.

Jerry went on, "Then we go down a ladder. You'll have to be careful. I don't want you to fall and get hurt."

The sawhorses set up to trip her in the dark? Maybe he didn't know what he wanted.

But she nodded, moved her bound hands against him.

"I can't. Not yet. I'll hold you. Don't worry. I won't let you fall."

He let go of her to slant one wing up, then braced it with a stick. He led her part way down the ladder, told her to wait and not move, and hurried up to drop the wing.

The white cat meowed at him. He clapped his hands and she scampered away.

He pulled the wing in. A bit of lilac leaf came with it. He picked it up, put it in his shirt pocket. Must leave no trace, he thought.

Once again, he held her, led her. "Be careful now. It's pitch-black, Jenny. I know you can't see. We'll have to duck and dodge around through here."

Again he smoothed her hair from her face. It was silkier than he remembered. He reminded himself that she was grown now. It had been a long time since he had touched her hair. Too long.

He was sweating by the time they had climbed the two flights of stairs. He held her so close that he could hear her raspy breath, feel her body warmth. The warmth tingled in him, became heat.

The room. He opened the door, thrust the heavy drapes aside. "I'll put on a light. You'll see the surprise I made for you, Jenny." He set her into a padded lounge chair, and found the matches, and lit the old-fashioned oil lamp. It had a red glass shade. The light it cast seemed red, too.

He saw that his hands were shaking, and stood there, holding on to the table edge, waiting. He would calm down. His heart would stop pounding. The roar in his ears would fade away. It was done. It was done just as it had come to him.

He turned to Quinn. "Jenny, it had to be this way."

She shook her head at him, gestured with her bound hands.

He went to her, leaned over. "You'll be good now? You promise? We have a lot to talk about, but I want you to be good."

She nodded, thrust her hands at him.

But he didn't touch them. He bent her head forward, smoothed the hair from the nape of her neck, and untied the cloth that held the gag in place. He pulled the gag from her mouth, smiling. "There. Isn't that better?"

She swallowed, moistened her lips, then whispered hoarsely, "You've made some crazy mistake. I'm Quinn Monroe."

"Jenny . . . please . . . No games. You *promised!*"

The room hung with red drapes so that there seemed to be no windows, no doors. No world beyond.

The two red lounge chairs. The mattresses with red coverlets. The table where the oil lamp burned red.

Quinn remembered now that Jenny had worn a red coat on the windy March evening she'd first come to the Wallowby to see about sharing the apartment. Quinn remembered her own red blouse that had disappeared.

"I'm not—" she began. But choked the words off.

Pink light glinted on the steel-rimmed glasses. His eyes were red, too. Red with rage. Wild, animal rage.

She held her breath. Go lightly, Quinn. The denial was wrong. Wait a little.

"Damn it," he said. "I don't want to hear any more of that stuff from you. Even if you did forget, you can listen to me, can't you? You can believe me. You're Jenny Lakas. And you've been away a long time. But now you're back. You're back with me. Your brother. Your brother Jerry."

Snowball was outside on her cat's business.

The groceries were in the car parked in the shed.

The silver buttons would soon be shining in the light of an end-of-May moon.

Quinn said softly, "I can't help it if I don't remember, Jerry."

The rage drained out of his eyes. He smiled faintly. "Well, I'm tired of it. It's got to stop. All this time I waited. Now I've found you. And it wasn't easy. So many things to do, to think and plan. So now you've got to start remembering. You've got to be you again. I don't care if you dyed your hair reddish and let it grow. That's okay with me. And I don't care if you look a little different. All right. Maybe it was a disguise and you wanted to be different. But that's over now. We're together. And you can be yourself again, can't you?"

Quinn breathed gently. Jenny Lakas had had a brother she'd never mentioned, parents of whom she'd never spoken. She'd been in hiding, though Quinn hadn't known it at the time. Why had Jenny hidden from her brother?

Quinn made herself yawn, seem casual. She stretched her legs, her bound arms. "Jerry?"

"Yes." It was sullen. His mouth drooped. His shoulders sagged.

In the red light and shadow his profile was completely recognizable now. Jerry Lakas had seen her in Michael's arms. He'd looked through shaggy spruce limbs and seen Michael and her be one.

She waited until she was sure of her voice. Then: "I guess you're right, Jerry. It'll come back to me. Just give me some time. But my hands are awfully tired. Couldn't you loosen them?"

"In a minute," he said gruffly. "There's something I want to do first."

"What's that, Jerry?"

"I'll tell you later." He went to the red drape. "Don't get up out of that chair while I'm gone, Jenny."

"All right."

"You promise? Cross your heart and hope to die?"

She sighed impatiently. "Okay. Sure. I promise I'll sit right here." It even sounded to her the way Jenny would sound.

He nodded, thrust the drape aside, and went out.

She rose halfway, then made herself sink down. No. No, not yet. A second's tick. Another.

He peered in at her, grinned. "Be right back." He disappeared again.

A rasp. The creak of stairs.

She waited, counting. One. Two. Three. Four. Five.

She got up from the lounge chair. Nothing. She approached the drape cautiously, listened. Nothing. He was gone.

With her bound hands, she thrust the drape aside. She tugged and pushed at the door latch. No movement. She remembered the rasp she'd heard. An outside bolt.

She turned instantly to make a swift circuit of the walls of the room. There were windows behind the red drapes. But they were boarded on the outside. No way to get at the nails. The floor was covered with a thick red shag rug. In the corner there was something that must be a camp stove. Near it, an ice chest. There'd be cutlery, she told herself. A knife. Something. She went to look. The knives and forks were plastic, pink, yellow, and red. The ice chest held food.

Beyond the door the stairs squeaked. She flung herself on the lounge as the bolt rasped.

He came in, carrying the groceries she had bought at Fieldstone's. He grinned. "No need to waste these." And: "We're really snug now. Nobody can bother us. I've set the alarm."

"The alarm, Jerry?"

"Sure. At the basement doors, so we'd know if they tried to get in."

"If who tried, Jerry?"

"They. *You* know."

Safer not to push that. Instead she asked, "We're going to stay here?"

"Sure." He busied himself putting the groceries away. Then he set a small transistor radio on the table. "We have everything we need, Jenny. And when we run out, or you want something, well, then, I'll just go get it."

"Stay here how long, Jerry?"

"It's where we live now," he answered. "You know . . . just the two of us . . . away from the world. Like . . . like hermits. Being together. Talking. Thinking. Like hermits. Only together."

"But,.Jerry, people will look for me. I can't disappear into thin air. And neither can you."

"I have," he laughed. "And so have you. There's no one left to look for us. Don't you remember what happened?"

"Happened?"

"In Washington."

"Washington, Jerry? I'm not sure it's come back to me yet. Maybe if you—"

"So there's nobody to look for you anymore."

She was thinking of Michael. He'll look. He won't wait too long. He'll never stop until he finds me. Michael.

"Your own roommate, Jenny. That nice girl you used to live with. You can't have forgotten her already."

"You mean Quinn?" she asked softly.

"Quinn. Yes. And not just her. The others, too."

"The others?" she murmured.

"Damn it, Jenny. Don't pretend anymore."

"But if you'd remind me a little—"

"Pa—he won't look for us. He can't stop us. He's dead, Jenny."

Quinn's eyes widened.

Jerry said, "I didn't touch him, and didn't have to. He just stared at me and fell down dead."

"In Washington?"

"Of course not." But he stopped, a bewildered look on his face. And then: "I guess it wasn't really Pa. It was the old man. In Wind-

sor. The big winner. I was going to get them all. For you, Jenny. Only for you."

The old man in Windsor. Nathaniel Gordon. Quinn tried to keep horror from her face.

"Because they were alive, and rich, and had everything," Jerry went on. But the words were tentative, puzzled. He was quiet for a moment, staring at her. At last he said, "In Washington it was your fancy doctor—that was different." He was suddenly rigid, glaring at her. "Don't lie about that, Jenny."

She said quickly, "I'm hungry. Why don't we eat?"

He relaxed. Pleasure flared in his eyes. He said happily, "It's about time you got hungry, and I have everything you like. Hot dogs and beans and cole slaw. And"—he jerked to a stop, midway across the room—"you do still like all that, don't you? I mean, your tastes haven't changed, have they?"

"I still like all that," she said.

He went to the stove and pumped it. He lit it with a match that he carefully dropped into a red glass on the table. He put two pans on the burners, filled one from a huge jug of water, the other with beans from a can. "Mustard for the beans," he muttered. "And an onion— oh, yes, here in the ice chest—"

"You have everything," she said admiringly. "How did you manage?"

"I spent a long time thinking about it," he told her. "Every angle. I wanted to be sure I worked it right."

"You did, too. All of it."

"Yes." He turned to look at her. "You're not angry with me any-more, are you?"

"Oh, no," she said. "I'm beginning to understand."

He stood still, staring at her. "I hope so. But I don't know. I wonder. You haven't always been so reasonable. What made you change, Jenny?"

"Me? Change?" She paused. She didn't know what to say. If he were suddenly to decide that she wasn't Jenny . . .

He waited. It was funny. The last time he spoke to her, she'd said, "Get away from me, Jerry. Leave me alone. I can't take anymore. I've tried and tried. It's wrong, I tell you, wrong." Her voice different, her eyes . . .

"So much happened," Quinn said carefully. "That's what made

me change, I think." And, grasping at straws, "All these months up here."

"It was silly of you, taking her name, moving here."

Quinn held her breath, but he didn't go on. She knew only that he imagined it was Quinn Monroe who had died in Washington.

He busied himself with his preparations. When he was done, he set out plates and plastic cutlery. "Let's eat."

She moved stiffly toward the table where the red-checked cloth seemed to shimmer under the lamplight. She sat in the chair across from him.

"You won't— Listen, Jenny, you won't do anything foolish, will you? I mean, you won't try to run away."

She shook her head.

"Because if you did—"

"I won't," she said quickly.

"Okay, then." He unbound her hands. "Better, isn't it?" And, at her nod: "Remember, you promised."

"I do."

"You couldn't anyhow. I wouldn't let you. And the windows are all boarded up, and the doors downstairs, too. The only way in is the way we came, and nobody knows about it. Besides, there's the alarm."

The alarm. Yes, Quinn thought. But Snowball knew. And a silver button lay close to the almost invisible wing doors near the lilac bush.

"And I guess you don't know how comfortable we'll be. There's even a chemical johnny and a tub, back behind that red curtain."

She looked where he pointed, nodded appreciatively, and began to eat. The hot dogs were cold, the beans, too. She forced the food down, knowing his eyes were fixed on her.

Finally he said, "I guess it doesn't matter even if you don't want to. We're going to be together anyhow."

"But I do," she answered. "Can't you tell that I do, Jerry?" She had eaten as much as she could force herself to. She put down her fork, tried to keep fright from showing in her eyes. He was mad.

"Do you remember how it was in Kenyon?" The culvert. Her slim tight body in his arms. Her teeth at his throat. He felt a throb in his groin.

"Kenyon? I guess I don't remember much from then."

"That's funny. You ought to. You were happy in Kenyon."

"Was I?"

"Of course you were. It was only when you went away to school, and left me behind, that things got spoiled. That's why they sent you there. To get you away from me. Pa did it all. It was his fault. He wanted you for himself. So he sent you away, and you met Ricky and turned against me. And don't say you've forgotten him."

"It's so long ago, Jerry."

"When he died, you said, 'Go away, Jerry. Leave me alone.' And I didn't see you anymore. Not for seven years."

Quinn shook her head sadly.

"Well, at least you remember your fancy Washington doctor with his fancy blue convertible. The one who gave you the diamond earclips and that expensive ring. That wasn't so long ago."

"Yes. Him. Not so long ago."

But Jerry's eyes had darkened. He said nothing for a long time. The room was silent. The lamplight flickered.

He was thinking that something was wrong. It wasn't the way it had bloomed in his head. Jenny wasn't the way he had imagined she would be. Something was wrong.

He got up, walked around the table, and stood over Quinn, looking down at her. He said, "It's different, but I don't know why." Taking her hand in his, he went on softly, "Why can't it be the way it used to?"

"I don't know, Jerry. Maybe because we're different."

"*I'm* not."

"Maybe you just don't realize it."

"No," he said harshly. "It's not that. I'm exactly the same. I haven't changed since the day they brought you home and put you into my arms and said that you belonged to me. You were my very own. My baby sister." He shook his head. "I haven't changed since the day you cuddled on me, and opened my pants, and kissed me, and called me scaredy cat when I cried. It's not me. It's you, Jenny. It started after the business with Ricky. When you ran away. And then, again, when I finally found you, you and your fancy doctor . . . You said it then, remember? 'Not again, Jerry. Oh, no—get away from me, Jerry.' And you ran away and went back to the apartment. You blamed me, always, always, you blamed me. But it was always us together. You know it was. It was for you that I killed them. Because you belong to me and always wanted to."

Someone named Ricky—a doctor in Washington—Quinn knew now

why Jenny had fled her brother, never mentioned her family in Kenyon. She knew why Jenny had killed herself.

"The way you people live," the black detective, Johnson had said. Separate. Uncaring. Unattached. With no trust. No need. No love. He had been describing Quinn Monroe.

Tears burned in her eyes. Life, flying into pieces never to be assembled. Chuck, turning away . . . The world at end when her parents died and he was gone, too. The painfully learned defense against a new hurt. The baggage she had brought with her to Elkhorn had been guilt. She'd lived with Jenny and never known what Jenny feared, and why she died.

An unnatural love for her brother . . . a long attempt to keep the ugly bond broken . . . a despairing recognition . . .

Quinn couldn't have known. And if she had, it wouldn't have mattered. She couldn't have changed the beginning or the end of Jenny's life.

"You're crying," Jerry said softly. "Are you sorry you ran away, Jenny?"

She nodded, afraid to speak. He'd killed three times before. Unless he'd imagined it. But no. That was one reason why Jenny had climbed the balcony and let go of the railing and fallen to her death. And Nathaniel Gordon was dead. That Quinn knew.

"I'm glad," Jerry said. "Only I wish you hadn't run away again. It seemed so long until I found you, and if it hadn't been for the lottery . . . But when I read about it, I knew."

"And you wrote me those nice letters."

"Yes. Just to tell you how glad I was. But that wasn't enough, so I had to come to see you. The way you disguised yourself . . . that job . . . poor Jenny. It was so silly of you to think you could get away. I was always with you. Always. The Capitol Hotel, in St. Mary's City. The Landing Motel in Jewell's Landing. The inn on Saugatuck Island . . ."

She avoided his eyes as she touched her bandaged knees, forced a faint smile. "That was naughty of you, Jerry. And spoiling my clothes, too."

"I'm sorry. I didn't mean to. I just wanted you to know I was there. And then—then—" He paused, a cloud over his face. A frown drawing his brows together. "There was some reason—"

"Because I'd run away. But I won't anymore." She glanced down at her watch. Six o'clock. Michael would be looking for her. He'd have gone to the State Police. Just a little more time. If they could find her—if they could approach the house without being seen . . . If . . .

She yawned widely.

He was staring at her. Something was wrong. He didn't know what it was. But he felt something. He had to wait and see. He had to be quiet and rest and let it happen to his mind.

She managed another casual yawn. "Jerry, do you mind if I take a nap?" She smiled. "It's been an exciting day for me."

"Sure," he said. "Go lie down."

She went to the lounge, stretched out, closed her eyes. This way they wouldn't talk. She'd make no mistakes in what she said. Time.

He covered her with a blanket.

"Thanks, Jerry."

"I don't want you to catch cold." He stood over her. "I hope you mean it, about forgiving me. Because—because I see I was wrong. It wasn't *them*. It was you. You turned against me, didn't you?"

Jenny had tried to break the relationship. It had been Jenny. Not the men she had been involved with. It was Jenny that he blamed now.

"This new one you've got, you don't have to worry about him," Jerry went on. "Because now, now that we're together, he doesn't matter anymore."

She nodded, said soberly, "It had nothing to do with him. You're right. Jerry, it was me all along. Only I see I was wrong. It's fate. You can't change fate."

"Fate. Yes," he answered.

Michael, she thought. If only we'd had more time together—if only I'd said yes to going in September—if only I hadn't been so afraid . . .

She lay very still, breathing evenly. After a moment or two, Jerry moved away.

The lamp went out suddenly. The room, when she looked, was pitch-dark. She heard him sigh. A small click. Music. A rustle. He was lying down, too.

She waited. It was important to create time. Michael would come. He would find her. She *knew*.

There was a whisper of movement. Jerry touched her face, smoothed back her hair. She pretended to be asleep.

Later he returned, stared down at her.

When he left her there was the rustling of the lounge as he settled himself, sighing.

Nothing happened. He waited to be lifted into the agonized pleasure he had known so few times before. He waited for the giant squeezing hand that would empty him of the consuming fire. Nothing happened.

He made himself imagine a small slick body in his arms. But it was no good. He slept a little, awakened, listened to Jenny's breath. Something was wrong. Faint memories drifted through his mind. An old man in a room in Windsor. In Riverside, a pretty girl with dark curly hair. St. Mary's City, and a tall slim blond woman, her pale face held high. The lucky ones. The winners. The two still ALIVE because there'd been no time yet. And his Jenny . . . ?

He awakened from sleep. The radio was still whispering. He got up. Stood over her. Saw that she slept.

The memories were gone now. Only questions remained.

He left the room, closing the bolt behind him. She said she'd forgiven him. She'd said she'd been wrong. She belonged to him. Fate had made it that way.

But how did he know? He crept down the two flights to the basement, made his way through the bulking shadows of debris left by families he'd never heard of, and climbed the ladder to the basement entry.

Above him the wings of the doors showed a thin line of pale sky. As he looked at it, he heard a faint meow.

He frowned. Now there was a padded scuffling of small claws. He slammed his fist into the wood. A quick scamper. A rustle in the brush. Okay.

He checked the alarm. Okay.

When he returned to the room, she said, "You know, Jerry, I've been thinking. It's going to be nice here for a while. But then we'll have to move on. We ought to think of where we'll be going."

"No," he said sullenly.

Lamplight pulsed in the room.

His shadow was tall, dark, threatening. Reflections blanked out the eyes behind his glasses.

She said, "If you really want to stay, all right. But I thought you'd like to go somewhere nicer with me."

He shook his head, turned the radio louder, and didn't speak again.

CHAPTER 27

The rising moon was silver. It outlined the gaunt frame of the empty house on the hill. Beyond it a thick layer of clouds was moving in from the ocean.

Michael looked at them, saying into the telephone, "Nothing?"

"Not yet," Lacy Pickett answered.

Michael put down the phone, shook his head when Helen lifted her brows.

"Taking too damn long," Bill Sears muttered.

"Yes," Michael agreed. His fault. Whatever happened to Quinn. He'd been too slow in seeing the danger, too slow in finding the truth.

Helen got up to walk restlessly around the living area.

She peered into the closet. She knelt to sweep an arm under the sofa. At last she said, "I wonder where Snowball is." She opened the door and yelled into the still night, "Here, puss. Here, Snowball."

There was no answering meow. She looked under her car. Michael's. Finally Quinn's apple-green Rabbit. No cat. She went in, muttering, "I want Quinn's Snowball here when she gets back." She put a saucer of milk on the doorstep.

Michael stared at the silver button he'd found near the car as if it were a crystal ball that would tell him where to go, where to look. He shoved it into his pocket. "I can't sit here and wait. I'm going to talk to Mrs. Varnick again."

"*We'll* go," Bill Sears said.

Helen put her face in her hands as they went out.

They didn't speak on the ride over. The neglected yard was dark. There was light on the first floor.

Michael knocked, and Mrs. Varnick peered at him from a side window.

She came at once to let him and Bill in.

"About your roomer . . ." Michael began.

"I told you, and I told Lacy. He's gone."

"It's where he's gone to that I'd like to know. Maybe you've remembered something by now."

And from Bill: "Like his favorite places."

"Only what I already said. How he was always going. Up to St. Mary's City and Ballston. Over to Saugatuck Island."

Bill and Michael exchanged glances. Lacy would have men checking the motels and inns and everything else in all those places and on the roads between.

Bill said, "Mrs. Varnick, can we look at his room?"

"Nothing there. He took everything with him. But if you want, sure, go on up. The front of the second floor."

Michael went first, found the light switch. It was a pleasant room, facing Old North Road. Wondering what he expected to find, he made a quick search, with Bill helping.

There was nothing. They went downstairs.

"I told you," Mrs. Varnick said. "He left it neat as a pin." She paused. Then: "Except for some mud. Which I swept up. Like mud off your shoes. He must have got that wandering around. A great one for that, Mr. Lakes. Had to know every lane and dirt track there was. Even asked me about Westbrook Road, when you know that doesn't go anyplace except to the house the government took."

"Westbrook Road," Michael repeated.

He and Bill broke for the door at the same time.

The car bottomed hard on the rocks.

"Slower. You can hear us ten miles off," Michael said.

Bill nodded, slowed momentarily, then picked up speed again. But he squinted ahead, swerving to miss the ruts. "Thank God for the moon. Just now, anyway."

Michael agreed, glanced at the sky. The cloud layer had drifted closer. There was a salty breeze off the ocean. "But we might be glad of dark when we get there."

Bill slowed, allowed the car to drift. Both men searched for the gap in the brush line that would mark the turn.

Neither of them saw the brief glitter of moonlight glancing off a silver button.

"Here," Michael said suddenly.

Bill cut left. A wheel ground the button into the dirt. The car rolled on.

The house rose suddenly against the sky, a blank and dark silhouette, silvered at carved gables.

Bill parked in the shadow of the trees.

He and Michael got out, walked silently to the edge of the meadow. There both went prone.

Michael made a soft exclamation as the brush near the house rippled, and something faintly white flashed away.

There was a glint of moonlight on the ground near the shed. A growl of thunder in the distance.

Michael inched forward. "Quinn's here, Bill. That's her cat."

"Careful. He'll see you moving if he's watching. You don't know what he'll do."

"He won't see me," Michael answered. He smeared a handful of dirt on his face, neck. He pulled his sweater well over his collar.

Bill did the same.

"The shed. To be certain." Michael went first, crawling on his belly.

Bill followed him. The meadow lay silent around them. The moon sank slowly behind the cloud layer. A new darkness shadowed them.

At the shed, behind a thick tangle of vines, there was a black automobile.

Bill muttered, "Something here," and plucked a silver button from the weeds.

"Tell Lacy," Michael said. "They'd better be quiet when they come in. Until they know what's happening."

Bill disappeared.

Michael eeled his way across the yard. He stopped when he saw the cat crouched under a lilac bush, licking her small paws.

His eyes burned. April Fools' Day . . . A moment when he knew his future, and Quinn's, hung in the balance. Devil buried. Quinn lay in her chair, pale, face wet with tears. Helen put the white kitten on her lap. He watched. Waited, suspended. If she refused the kitten, then he and the future were refused. But she took the small white bundle to her warmth. And he breathed again. He'd have her.

He raised his eyes to the gaunt outline of the house. He'd have her, he told himself now.

The salty breeze had become quick uneven gusts. The weeds around him rustled. Safe to move. He went in a slow wriggle to the cinderblock basement walls. No way to be seen there from inside the house.

He rubbed more dirt on his face, hands, the back of his neck. He secured his collar under his dark sweater so no white showed. Rising, he stepped out of his shoes.

No moon now. Only the dark. The wind. On silent stockinged feet, he made a slow tour, checking windows and doors at the ground level. All boarded. Nailed.

But there must be a way in.

Quinn was there. Inside. With Jerry Lakas.

Back to the shed side. Snowball still sat beneath the arch of the lilac bush. Her purr was covered by a crackle of lightning, a drumroll of nearing thunder.

Some way in. The cat clawed at the mat of leaves beneath her feet.

Michael went prone again, eeled to the place, and saw the outline of the wing doors.

Hand instantly out to open. It froze. Ambush! It had to be, since it was the only way in.

Snowball made a playful pass at his face. He murmured at her, eeled away.

When he rose, close to the house again, he caught the faint glow of red light edging a boarded window on the second floor. The room. It would be two flights up from the ground, three from the basement.

He toured the house once again. He'd make a way in.

He took out his pocket knife. A fork of lightning close by. Moments of explosive thunder. He used them to dig one nail from a sealed door. Patience. The storm was on his side. The noise covering the noise he made. But he was careful. Too much at risk. Quinn. Jerry Lakas—mad.

At last the door free, the lock giving way beneath the knife blade.

He stepped into darkness, carefully closed the door, wedged it so that the wind couldn't blow it open to sound an alarm.

That reminded him. He drifted with the dark until he found the stairs that led to the basement.

Feeling ahead with hand and foot, he made his way down the steps and through the debris that filled his path. He found the ladder to the wing doors by stumbling on it. It was a soundless hitch. He froze, listened.

Silence within the house. Outdoors, eruptions of thunder.

Ambush. He climbed the ladder carefully. He found the wire that led from the doors above his head. It was hooked to a spring attached to a clapper soldered to what seemed to be a large pizza pan. He cut the wire. Broke the spring. Ripped the clapper away.

Two entrances for Lacy and his men. They'd find them. They'd know the room by the red that glowed at the boarded window.

Michael made his way, a dark-faced ghost, back to the first floor. Two more flights of stairs. Each step tested with his palm before being given his weight.

Midway on the third, he saw ahead a faint line of red beneath a door.

He held his breath, moved close. A bolt hung open. From within, the whisper of voices. No words. No identities. Voices.

His hand went out. But once again, it froze. Ambush?

If Jerry Lakas had a gun, a knife. If Quinn were bound . . . What would happen in that brief instant when Michael flung the door open?

Thunder exploded. But no lightning flickered within the sealed house. All was dark.

Outside there must be diversion. Lacy, his men, the quiet cars. The two ways in.

Michael withdrew to the deepest of shadows near the door, blended with them. Wait.

The red room shook with thunder.

". . . On this beautiful spring day tragedy struck in Passamody," the radio newscaster said. "The body of a young girl was found strangled in the dock area. State Police have no clues to her identity. And, even closer to home, here in Elkhorn, State Police are attempting to learn the whereabouts of Quinn Monroe, of Old Barn Road, winner of one hundred thousand dollars in the lottery numbers draw last February, whose car was found near her home at approximately four thirty today."

Jerry sat very still. The radio continued its whispers, but he no longer listened.

A girl found strangled in the dock area at Passamody . . . Quinn Monroe disappeared in Elkhorn . . .

Quinn Monroe.

She had sent Jenny's clothing home, and said she was sorry Jenny had died. She had won the lottery, and lived. Quinn Monroe still lived.

Pictures flickered before his eyes. Quinn, red-gold hair flowing down her back, fading into Jenny. Blurring outlines of body and voice. Melting together, separating. Long slim legs and narrow hips . . . A man's wide shoulders. Jenny rising from where Quinn had lain.

He turned his head slowly. She was standing beside the table.

It was all in his mind, in clear detail. Every move.

He got to his feet, started toward her. Started toward Quinn Monroe, who lived, while Jenny had died.

Quinn saw past the red light shining in his glasses. She saw the dawning in his eyes. She knew.

She said, "I tried to tell you, Jerry." And turning, but very slowly, with her back to the lantern so that he could hardly see her face, "But I couldn't make you believe me. I knew you'd figure it out for yourself soon. I'm nothing like Jenny." Saying whatever came into her mind. Speaking in a quick hushed voice. Her hand went back, behind her. Fumbled for the lantern. "Jerry, whatever happened in the beginning? I mean when you and Jenny were kids. That spoiled everything for both of you?"

And, as he sprang at her, bringing the lantern up, hot oil spilling on her fingers.

Bringing it up and over her head and flinging it at him with all her strength.

A flash.

She spun away in fiery brilliance.

He screamed, pawing at his face, his chest.

She didn't see. The room whirled in flame. Drapes ablaze.

The door?

Where was the door?

She ran, a fiery thing lunging behind her. Blistering hands clutched her shoulders. Screaming, she kicked out.

A flaming drape billowed. A fiery darkness beyond the suddenly open door.

Michael! She knew it was he.

She broke free of the burning thing that was Jerry Lakas, and screamed, through a raw throat, "He was going to kill me, Michael, and I threw the lantern at him!"

Even as Michael's reaching arm enclosed her, his hands patted live embers from her hair and throat and plucked scorched fabric from her breasts. Even then, as he spun away from the shrill wail of encompassing death, and leaped half the stairs and fell the rest, he crooned, "I've got you. You're safe now. Oh, Christ, you're safe, Quinn."

And she was saying, "He told me when he thought I was Jenny. He's killed so many times. Two men at least that Jenny loved. And poor old Nathaniel. Because he was a winner. And then—then he realized—"

Still murmuring, "But you're okay. I've got you," Michael reached open air, and salty wind, and a sky that flickered with faded lightning.

He flailed a path across the meadow toward cars and armed men, and hooks and ladders with pump wagons, responding to the blaze.

Behind them, the house that had been her hell crumbled slowly into the scorched earth.

A murmur of voices. Bright lights dimly sensed. She opened her eyes.

Michael was there.

She was salved, bandaged, sedated and floating with it. There was something she had to tell him. Important. She tried to form words through numb lips.

. . . The bad days after her parents died . . . Chuck Ford, her school friends, all too young to help her in her grief . . . How she taught herself that loneliness was freedom because any closeness might bring her further pain . . . Jenny's reaching toward her . . . Quinn's uneasy half-response, half-retreat . . . The guilt that followed Jenny's death . . . Jerry, speaking softly in the red room of incestuous love, and murder . . . Quinn finally learning what lay behind Jenny's mask, and why she killed herself . . . The lottery win that had drawn Jerry to Quinn, to Elkhorn, because she was alive and lucky, when Jenny was dead . . . The madness that made dead Jenny alive in Quinn for him . . . The hatred when he knew it wasn't so . . . How hearing his whispers cleansed her . . . Fear burned away by the fire that had killed him . . . How, even in terror, she had believed in Michael . . . known he would come . . . How she had flung the lantern because there were chances to be taken . . . Need and love remained . . .

Michael. She managed to whisper it.

He bent closer. "I'm here, Quinn."

She drowsed off, faintly hearing a word. "Always."

Had he said it? Or had she? She wasn't sure.

CHAPTER 28

A cool September wind swept across the Passamody airfield, ruffling Michael's hair and tugging at Quinn's scarf. She tucked it into her collar to hide the faintly pink burn scar on her throat. A wedding band gleamed on her finger.

She smiled, imagined a bright spinning globe. The world she would explore. But not alone. Michael was part of the lifelong dream made real by her lottery win.

Soon they were aloft. Within moments, she saw below them the autumn-red maples of Elkhorn, where the nightmare had begun and ended, with the memory of Jenny finally laid to rest.

When Elkhorn disappeared, she looked toward the horizon, and reached for Michael's hand.

EPILOGUE

STATE LOTTERY COMMISSION
SEMI-ANNUAL REPORT TO STATE ASSEMBLY dated August
21, 1978, for the period between January 1, 1978, and June 30, 1978.

Total lottery tickets sold:	4,188,901
Net revenues to date:	$5,723,421
State share calculated to date:	$2,102,348
Obligated prize fund to date:	$7,925,113

REPORT OF STATE ASSEMBLY JOINT COMMITTEE ON
ALLOCATION OF LOTTERY REVENUE, dated September 21,
1978, for estimated revenues for the period between January 1, 1978,
and June 30, 1978.

Highway repair (estimated):	$1,000,000
Aid to education:	500,000
Capital construction:	600,000
Mental health	
Division of Retardation	
Held for future projects:	2,348